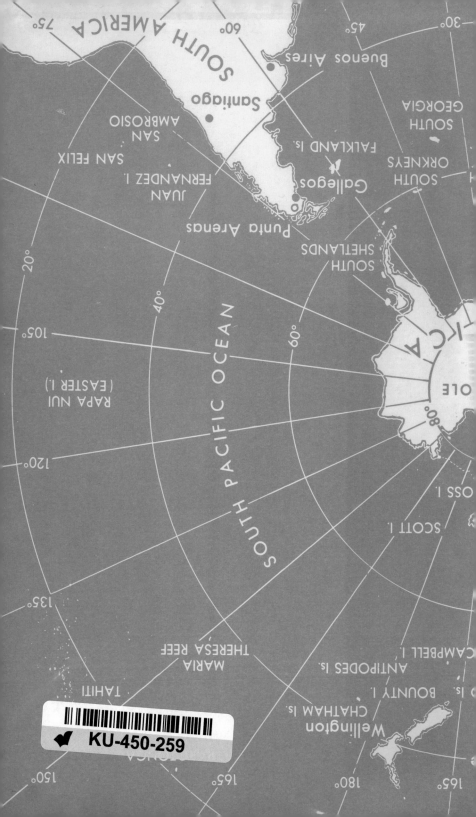

# THE FAR SOUTH

*The Far South* is a book about Antarctica by a man who, as an officer of ANARE, has lived there for three terms, and who can also draw on his personal knowledge of the experiences of others and on a devoted reading of the classics of antarctic literature. His account, vigorous and wide-ranging, covers the history of Antarctica, its physical make-up and climate, its bird and animal life, and the important scientific work that has been carried on; and includes a thoughtful discussion of its potentialities. On the human side, the author gives many details of day-to-day life in a climate where tepid water freezes in a heap when poured to the ground. What it is that draws men to the Antarctic, a powerful sense of its beauty, majesty and terror, is implicit in the whole book.

# THE FAR SOUTH

*by*

JOHN BÉCHERVAISE

*With a foreword by*
PHILLIP LAW

ANGUS AND ROBERTSON

*First published in Great Britain in 1962 by*

ANGUS AND ROBERTSON LTD

54-58 Bartholomew Close, London
89 Castlereagh Street, Sydney
66 Elizabeth Street, Melbourne
168 Willis Street, Wellington

Registered in Australia for transmission by post as a book
PRINTED IN AUSTRALIA BY HALSTEAD PRESS, SYDNEY

# ACKNOWLEDGMENTS

I record my gratitude for the friendship and inspiration of the late Sir Douglas Mawson, who read my original draft and, on the day before he died, wrote wishing success to *The Far South*.

My thanks are also due to Phillip Law, Director of ANARE, for providing a foreword; to him and to Dr Fred Jacka, Head of the ANARE Research Staff, for looking over the book in typescript; and to the various expedition men whose photographs are acknowledged where they appear.

J. M. B.

# FOREWORD

SINCE 1947 the ANARE has built up in Australia a reserve of adventurous men with sound experience in antarctic techniques of exploration and research. Of these, none is more qualified to speak with authority about Antarctica than John Béchervaise, who has served three separate terms as Officer-in-Charge of ANARE stations.

In September 1952 John Béchervaise joined the staff of the Antarctic Division as O.I.C. of the 1953 Heard Island party. His interest in mountain-climbing was stirred by the challenge of Big Ben, the unscaled icy nine-thousand-foot sentinel of the southern Indian Ocean. Although defeated in his attempt to conquer this mountain, he and two companions reached a point higher than any others have yet achieved. At the Heard Island Station itself his flair for organization and leadership resulted in a highly successful and productive year.

With his appetite for adventure whetted rather than diminished by the experience, Béchervaise returned to Melbourne in 1954 eager for service farther south. At this time we had just established a tentative foothold at Mawson, in MacRobertson Land, where R. G. Dovers and nine others were probing for the first time an unknown area of ice and mountains which later was to prove one of the most interesting areas of rock exposure in Antarctica. With this foothold firmly established and the bridgehead secured, our next move was to feed in the elaborate scientific programmes which were three years later to become the basic studies of the International Geophysical Year. Béchervaise was appointed O.I.C. of the 1955 Mawson party and his tour of duty marked the development of the station as a major scientific observatory.

To those who have not witnessed it, there is something almost incredible in the results that a group of energetic, vigorous men, welded into an efficient team, can accomplish in an uninterrupted year of effort at an antarctic station. During 1955 Mawson grew from an outpost of five huts to a small village of seventeen buildings. The pioneer programme of work on meteorology and geology was expanded to include cosmic radiation, auroral observations, geomagnetism, seismology, gravity, glaciology and biology. With vehicles much less suitable than those later developed, and without the benefit of aircraft (which were not introduced until 1956), Béchervaise and his men pushed far afield and set foot for the first time in the northern ranges of the Prince Charles Mountains, which had been sighted from a distance and named by Robert Dovers in the preceding year.

With a year of solid accomplishment and rich adventure behind him, any ordinary man might have been expected to retire from the life of toil and hardship which constitutes the lot of an antarctic leader; but to a man young in heart and vigorous in enthusiasm the antarctic environment loses nothing of its appeal by acquaintance, and after three years of civilized comforts and urban pleasures Béchervaise once again returned to Antarctica as leader of a Mawson party, this time with an even more comprehensive programme of research and exploration.

Before sailing he gave me the manuscript of this book, suggesting that if I considered it worth while I might agree to pass it to a publisher and add a short foreword.

It is a pleasure for me to write these few words to preface the work of a man whose qualities I have always admired and whose friendship I am proud to claim, for few men to-day have the personal experience and broad knowledge of Antarctica which John Béchervaise by his strenuous efforts has acquired.

PHILLIP LAW

# CONTENTS

# ILLUSTRATIONS

# MAPS

# INTRODUCTION: THE PROSPECT

ANTARCTICA is an immense continent with an area of more than 5,000,000 square miles. Just to compare it in extent with other great continents—Australia (less than 3,000,000 square miles) or Europe (including U.S.S.R. as far east as the Ural Mountains, 3,800,000 square miles)—or with such an important country as the United States (3,600,000 square miles) is to discover a very good reason why the rest of the world wants to know as much about it as possible. In this little volume we shall consider how explorers of various nations took up its challenge to satisfy their essential human curiosity and that of the world, and discuss Australia's interest and activity in the region over many years.

In 1947 the word ANARE, abbreviating Australian National Antarctic Research Expeditions, came into common use. Ever since then, augmenting the earlier work of Sir Douglas Mawson and his teams, there has been an unbroken period of Australian scientific exploration in the far south. When the nations were mustering for the International Geophysical Year (June 1957-December 1958) Australia was already represented at Mawson, undertaking a comprehensive geophysical programme that included studies of the aurora and of cosmic rays. Two of the largest cosmic-ray telescopes in the world had been installed there early in 1955. When the I.G.Y. was over, Australia continued her scientific work and exploration in the Antarctic with undiminished vigour. Today three ANARE bases in the Antarctic and one at Macquarie Island are more active than ever.

The south polar regions include the highest, coldest and stormiest continent on earth. For millions of years almost the whole surface of that land has lain beneath an overburden of ice thousands of feet thick. It revolves round the

South Pole like a white hub-cap of our planet, separated from the inhabited lands by the world's loneliest oceans. These facts, of course, have made its discovery and exploration extremely difficult, often dangerous, and generally uncomfortable. In the first chapter we shall go back in time, and dream, with the old philosophers and voyagers, of a fabled Terra Australis or Great South Land. We shall follow the noble journeys of intrepid men who conquered their fear of endless empty oceans and utter loneliness and, to replace fancy and fiction, charted the limits of two great tracts, Australia and Antarctica.

The high antarctic plateau that rises abruptly from the sea is for the most part a lifeless desert of ice and snow where the temperatures remain perpetually below freezing point. Not even the lichens (belonging to primitive orders of flowerless plants) that in summer brighten the coastal rocks can survive more than a few miles beyond the boundaries of the bitter plateau possessing an average height twice that of mountainous Asia. No account of Antarctica would be complete without some mention of Nature's prolonged and constant efforts to maintain life in the seas along the coasts. The most familiar symbol of Antarctica is a penguin, the creature which, in order to sustain life through millions of years of slow climatic change, evolved wings for flight under water, and flesh to insulate it from temperatures too low for any other bird on earth. How does the northern Arctic differ from these southern polar regions, apart from being the only natural haunt of the white polar bear? Why are there neither Eskimos nor bears in the Antarctic, nor any parallel forms of life?

In the Antarctic there are grey weeks of morose howling blizzard when the air is opaque with minute streaming particles of snow, and days of extraordinary silence, brilliant light and an atmosphere so clear that nothing is hidden except by crests of ice or the curvature of the earth. Abrupt mountain ranges, bleak and bare beyond imagination, thrust through a mile or more of ice. The immeasurable quantities of drifting snow which stream past their summits are always too cold and dry to adhere to their rock. Why is the weather so different from that of the inhabited continents? Why is there daylight in summer for months on end, with corresponding periods of winter gloom? Of what rocks are the harsh mountains formed? What is the cause of the deep dark cracks in the ice which we call crevasses? And how on earth did such an enormous mantle of ice ever get there in the first place? We must answer these and many more questions of this kind.

It does seem rather odd, on the face of it, that, in spite of all the accounts of discomforts and dangers, there has never been a time when more men have ventured, through the stormy seas and drifting bergs and pack ice, in to Antarctica. After nearly fifty years British explorers again have reached the South Pole over the surface of the plateau; daring Americans, having landed from aircraft, were in a comfortable base there, under the midnight sun, to greet them. It is of great interest to us, surely, that, for the entire duration of the trans-polar journey, an Australian scientific party was also travelling over the plateau, making an equally important contribution to science; and that, in the loneliest part of all Antarctica, a Russian base was set up at that time too, in a common cause of science. These expeditions have been seeking the answers to questions such as I have already propounded. Especially was the I.G.Y. a focus of effort for the new scientific explorers of all nations, in a world which realizes that truth may not be partitioned. For many years the results of the I.G.Y. will be used for research into the nature of the earth and its atmosphere and the physical forces that govern our existence. A modern account of the "great white south" must speak of aspects of science unknown no less than of territories unexplored at the beginning of the twentieth century, and use many terms then uncoined.

Finally, for our consideration, there is still the future of

Antarctica and the southern circum-polar seas. What is there
beyond the calls of pure science and adventure? These, one
trusts, will always attract Australians. What else may eventually make the least hospitable region on earth of importance to mankind? Is it important that men and women strive
against odds merely, in the final analysis, as a human gesture?
My final task in this small book will be an attempt to answer
such questions.

# 1

# THE SEARCH FOR ANTARCTICA

It is always pleasing to our sense of order when we have clear beginnings and endings in history; they make it so much easier to fill in the gaps and trace developments in a proper time scale. The need for order is probably the only real reason why, in accounts of exploration in the southern hemisphere, old Greek fancies and early medieval superstitions supporting the presence of a great continent to balance the landmasses of Europe and Asia are so often mentioned. After all, once the idea of a spherical earth had occurred to men about two and a half thousand years ago, the filling in of blank spaces was bound to occur. Empty wastes of sea would seem illogical. Even in fairly modern times it was fashionable to cover unexplored areas on the maps of "dark" continents like Africa and Australia with pictures of beasts and birds and natives in strange guises. The famous map showing the voyage of van Neck to the East Indies as late as 1600 depicts a great sagacious elephant bestriding Terra Australis Incognita just where our modern Cape York is clearly recognizable.

Aristotle (384-322 B.C.) considered the world a globe and Eratosthenes of Cyrene, a hundred years later, is credited with the invention of a system of latitude and longitude for his maps. He also held the earth to be spherical, and this hypothesis, doubtless based on the circular shadow of the earth at the moon's eclipse, remained amongst the wise at least until the time of the great geographer Ptolemy, who lived in Alexandria about the year A.D. 150. By then Europe, the Mediterranean and Africa were all known more or less clearly (it is fairly certain that Africa had been rounded by the Phoenicians, although Ptolemy doesn't show this). It was natural that on representations of a globe the landmasses of the old world should be "balanced" by hypothetical lands beyond the Pillars of Hercules in the west, and in the far south.

All these rich theories and speculations slept nearly a thousand years through the dark ages following the decline of Rome and her great empire. They were awakened during the early Renaissance by tales of the remarkable journeys of the Polos—Marco, his father Nicolo, and his uncle Maffeo —all of whom returned to their native Venice towards the end of the year 1295 after an absence of twenty-five years spent in China and in journeying to and from the court of Kublai Khan. They had visited Tibet, India, Burma, Persia, Malaya and even the coasts of Sumatra. Polo's tales were exaggerated and misunderstood; they were used freely to support men's fondest hopes. Eventually, of course, many of the old theories and accounts of the ancient world also came to light to buttress the prevailing spirit of inquiry.

It is likely that in the meantime Norse longboats had reached America and there had been wide voyaging by Polynesians in the Pacific. These were probably entirely outside our cultural stream and have only been appreciated in modern times. Still, it is just possible that rumours of such exploits, hopelessly distorted, travelled down through Europe with the bearers of carved walrus tusks or up from the East Indies with the Polos.

The centuries pass and Vasco da Gama and Magellan make for us a newer, more definite, starting point in modern geographical discovery. Africa was rounded (1497) and the world was circumnavigated (1519-22). But still, always just beyond the southern limits of these tremendous voyages, there persisted in the minds of men and on the maps of sixteenth-century cartographers a great southern continent. As part of this fancy, Magellan's Tierra del Fuego, south of his stormy strait, really lasted only fifty years, until Drake was driven far to the south in 1577 and sighted Cape Horn, where the Atlantic and Pacific oceans freely mingled, with nothing visible southward beyond.

In 1605 the mystical Fernandez de Quiros set sail with the blessing of Philip III of Spain to explore the coasts of Terra Australis (wherever they might be!). He reached the New Hebrides (later so named by Captain Cook), about which he made extravagant claims, stubbornly asserting that islands were continents, and took possession, on behalf of his King and his Church, of all land southward in the world, naming it Austrialia del Espiritu Santo. Torres, who had been with de Quiros, sailed westward when his captain's vessel, probably suffering mutiny, returned to Peru. He passed between New Guinea and Australia and so further reduced the possible bounds of Terra Australis, although, in fact, his discoveries did not become known for many years.

Dutch navigators bound for the East Indies and an occasional British freebooter—Dirck Hartog, Pelsaert, Nuyts, Tasman, Dampier are just a few of these voyagers who were of particular significance to Australia—either on course or off, still further curtailed the boundaries, if not the hopes, of the desired continent. Tasman, by sailing south of New Holland (Australia) in 1642, thrust the possible northern limits of additional southern land thousands of miles beyond those imagined by de Quiros. However, having touched Tasmania, he discovered the western coasts of New Zealand and considered that they might be part of a vast continent stretching south and east. His second voyage, however, only confirmed the current Dutch opinions of New Holland—a bare, barbarous, unpleasant and unprofitable place. Nor was William Dampier impressed in 1688 and 1699.

His and the Dutch views remained current until Cook observed, with somewhat greater enthusiasm, the eastern coast of Australia between April and August in 1770, soon after he had disproved New Zealand's connection with any larger landmass. So extraordinarily successful was this voy-

4

age of James Cook that he was commissioned by the British
Government to venture southward again in order to settle,
once and for all, whether any other continents existed in the
Antipodes. A further task was to forestall the French who,
at least since Bouvet's discoveries in 1738-9—when he saw
seals and penguins, probably on the island (lat. 54°S., long.
5°W.) which now bears his name—had taken a great interest
in the possibilities of an empire in the south. The gallant
Bougainville was ahead of Cook; also poor Kerguelen, who,
rather like de Quiros, thought his desolate islands in the sub-
antarctic Indian Ocean were part of a new El Dorado; and
there was Marion du Fresne also busy in the same sector of
the cold south seas.

On his second voyage (1772-5) Cook circumnavigated the
world in high southern latitudes. In a series of magnificent
probes he established that no land could possibly exist to
bridge the temperate and frigid zones of the hemisphere.

It would be difficult to imagine a task of such magnitude
being done more thoroughly or more doggedly. Anyone who
knows the pack ice and bergs of the Antarctic must marvel
at the tenacity of Cook. His *Resolution* (462 tons) and the
even smaller *Adventure* (under Tobias Furneaux), with
about two hundred men, not only crossed the Antarctic
Circle (lat. 66°32'S.) for the first time (17th January,
1773) but, though constantly rebuffed by ice, headed southward beyond this latitude twice more during the next summer. I have voyaged through antarctic waters several times
in what were thought small vessels, but the least of these,
the Norwegian *Tottan*, was 540 tons, of steel, with powerful
diesel engines, a radio voice to speak with the world and
a radar eye to scan the dark or distant dangers of the sea.
And, when we rolled over in storms and saw the merciless
cliffs of great icebergs, I thought of Cook and others whose
sole power was from wind and current and whose sole salva-
tion lay in faith, courage and seamanship.

Cook's first meeting with the ice, after five stormy months

in the Atlantic, was almost directly south of Africa. That year the pack ice must have extended unusually far to the north, and before Cook reached a latitude of 51°S. (the corresponding parallel in the northern hemisphere cuts through the south of England!) he was faced by ice-floes in every direction. He retired northwards, returned to the attack, and celebrated Christmas still making seaway amongst the bergs. At his farthest south in this operation he was only a few hundred miles due west of where the Australian (ANARE) research station of Mawson was established a hundred and eighty-one years later. Had ice conditions forced Cook to make his probe only a little more to the west he might well have reached the antarctic continent, for he was already farther south than the two-hundred-mile bulge of Enderby Land.

It must be remembered that Cook had no way of knowing whether the tremendous ice-fields heaving and scraping against his wooden hull were, somewhere in the misty distance, backed by land. His surmise was that land "wholly covered" by ice that had been there "from the earliest time" existed to his southward. And he was, as we now know, absolutely right. In most parts of Antarctica ice-cliffs, indistinguishable from the flat icebergs they spawn, are the only coastline. If Cook had sighted the long white line in the distance, either by direct vision through the incredibly clear atmosphere that is sometimes found, or by the fantastic optical system of the polar mirage, nothing could have afforded him any clue to its true identity. Even John Biscoe, the whaler, who discovered in 1831 the land Cook so narrowly missed and named it after his employers, the Enderbys, in fact approached the coast no more closely than twenty or thirty miles and was not certain, even then, whether his Enderby Land was part of the antarctic mainland.

After the exploration of antarctic ice in the African sector, Cook searched for Kerguelen's Land and the islands of Marion. He did not find them, which at least proved that

Kerguelen's eager dreams of having discovered a vast domain for France would never materialize. I often used to wonder just how close Cook sailed to the forlorn grey ice-cap of Heard Island, where I wintered in 1953. That island had been discovered and forgotten a couple of times before Captain Heard sighted it in 1853. The seas of the 'fifties are the most tempestuous in the world, and the storm barrier of those latitudes has been the first hazard of antarctic exploration in every period.

The great English navigator took his vessels south again to the sixtieth parallel and did not leave high latitudes until he turned their bows for New Zealand and the imaginary Austrialia del Espiritu Santo of de Quiros, which, naturally, he didn't find. After spending a southern winter in the Pacific, amongst the ever-fascinating south sea islands (which eventually, on 14th February, 1779, claimed his life), Cook made further polar journeys. First he crossed the Antarctic Circle in December 1773, having been in contact with ice, off and on, for about a thousand miles of the voyage. He thrust on amidst the pack ice until it again seemed madness, but Cook left the grey bergs only for a month, in order to make quite sure that there was no great south Pacific continent lying between his present route and that of his 1769 voyage; then he returned south with magnificent resolution.

The second Pacific probe took him farther south than ever before, to lat. 71°10'S., in long. 106°54'W. (about directly south of Easter Island, which he later visited), on 30th January, 1774. The vessels then abutted massed floes ranging beyond the southern horizon. It was at this time that Cook wrote, most memorably:

I will not say it was impossible any where to get farther to the South; but the attempting it would have been a dangerous and rash enterprise, and what, I believe, no man in my situation would have thought of. It was, indeed, *my* opinion, as well as the opinion of most on board, that this ice extended quite to the pole, or perhaps joined to some land, to which it had been fixed from the earliest time. . . . And yet I think there must be some [land] to the South behind this ice; but if there is, it can afford no better retreat for birds, or any other animals, than the ice itself, with which it must be wholly covered. I, who had ambition not only to go farther than any one had been before, but as far as it was possible for man to go, was not sorry at meeting with this interruption, as it, in some measure, relieved us; at least, shortened the dangers and hardships inseparable from the navigation of the southern polar regions. Since therefore we could not proceed one inch farther to the South, no other reason need be assigned for my tacking and standing back to the North. . . .

Not for another fifty years was Cook's latitude surpassed —and then it was by another British navigator, James Weddell, who had been with the navy that Cook had served.

The third January of this magnificent voyage again saw Cook in the Antarctic after a second wintering in the Pacific (it was during this period that, as the New Hebrides, he renamed simply and suitably the grandiose Austrialia of de Quiros). This time he rounded Cape Horn from the west, annexed South Georgia and discovered the South Sandwich Islands in the Atlantic sector. There remained no part of the southern hemisphere that could possibly hold unknown continents. Cook has been hailed as the discoverer of Australia, which is, of course, an honour he would never have withheld from the Dutch; it is far odder, really, that he has not been given the credit for discovering Antarctica. The two contestants for that distinction according to modern research— Edward Bransfield and Nathaniel Palmer—never sailed anything like so far south, nor, any more than their successors for many years, did they set foot on the antarctic mainland. But, in following up Cook's reports of vast seal colonies on antarctic islands, they did apparently both sight the tip of the peninsula of Graham Land, outside the Antarctic Circle, and this, after a hundred and twenty years of doubt, was almost conclusively proved by the Australian John Rymill part of the antarctic mainland.

Cook wrote in another frequently quoted passage:

> Lands doomed by Nature to perpetual frigidness; never to feel the warmth of the sun's rays; whose horrible and savage aspect I have not words to describe. Such are the lands we have discovered; what then may we expect those to be, which lie still farther to the South? . . . If anyone should have resolution and perseverance to clear up this point by proceeding farther than I have done, I shall not envy him the honour of the discovery; but I will be bold to say, that the world will not be benefited by it.

We must try to bridge the gap between Cook's time and our own and discover just why men turned their backs on safety and comfort and continued to dare storm and berg and sea ice. But of more than a century I must write briefly, for, although voyage after voyage was made in antarctic waters, each one served only to augment the discoveries of Cook without modifying his basic theory of a great ice-sheathed antarctic continent. Each log virtually retells much of Cook's original story; each chart delineates only a little that is new and certain. Slowly the continental ice-cliffs cease to recede as the vagaries of season permit men to sail farther south here or there; never is there any assurance in "the pack". Always there is caprice, in season and in ice—for the steel ships of ANARE, with their relatively vast power, as for the *Resolution* and the *Adventure*, stout sailing vessels of wood.

# 2

## SEALERS AND SCIENTISTS

BEFORE speeding forward through time to the Antarctica of the ageing twentieth century, let us consider some encounters which further defined the problems of the south. We may then be in a better position to realize that the powers of weather and ice, in spite of jets and electronics, are still as capricious and capable of dealing disaster as in the days of Cook or Balleny, Scott or Mawson. In one sense all antarctic explorers are contemporary, for the continent they visit does not change in man's scale of time; and our modern mastery over space often seems merely to make more comprehensible the vastness and loneliness of the antarctic plateau and the polar seas.

I do not want to trace in detail all the expeditions, great and small, or the odd ventures and voyages that, after James Cook, accomplished little or much, towards clarifying our knowledge of Antarctica. This has been often attempted and I shall list sufficient references at the end of this book for you to cover the ground more completely if you wish. I shall confine myself, in this chapter, to the broad canvas, dwelling briefly on the highlights, which reveal the pattern of antarctic discovery more clearly than a precise chronological account.

On 16th February 1875, exactly one hundred years after Cook steered north from the pack ice for the last time, the first steam-powered vessel to cross the Antarctic Circle,* H.M.S. *Challenger*, still voyaged in mysterious waters. For one thing, observers on board could find no trace of the continent reported in 1840 in those parts by the explorer Charles

* In long. 78°22′E.

Wilkes; yet from the sea-floor were dredged up rocks that proved beyond doubt that such a continent did exist. The land in that area remained a phantom for many years after Wilkes's voyage. Though he must surely have been mistaken, and perhaps culpably, about the nature and position of his reported coasts, more recent historians do not doubt his integrity. There were certainly still immense difficulties of travel in polar seas, quite apart from hazards of ice and exposure. For mirages lifted white lands above the horizon, then as now (as I have myself seen while sledging on sea ice west of Mawson), and men could not believe their eyes; chronometers were subjected to low temperatures with unknown results; there were no radio time-signals to enable a navigator to be quite certain of his longitude. Aeroplanes, to discover ways through the pack ice ahead of the ship and to examine and photograph the coast and establish its nature indisputably, from vertically above, were still very far away —beyond that day of 16th November 1928 when the Australian Sir Hubert Wilkins made the first antarctic flight. Just imagine! Within a month he had flown poleward six hundred miles in a single day and seen much more of the Graham Land peninsula than anyone in history.

The *Challenger*, in three and a half years cruising sixty-nine thousand miles, was undertaking a scientific investigation of the oceans of the world, foreshadowing the essential global approach of modern geophysics.

It was not science, however, that motivated antarctic exploration during most of the nineteenth century. Captain Cook had reported innumerable seals at South Georgia, and, within three or four years, British adventurers had begun to hunt them with great profit. The skins of fur seals (more will be said about antarctic animals in Chapter 6) were always in great demand in both Europe and Asia and for many years the exact sources of the most prolific supplies were jealously guarded secrets. As the seal population on Cook's South Georgia and the South Sandwich Islands fell, efforts were made to discover new rocky coasts that might buttress the lucrative trade. At the same time the value of the oil from other species, especially the ponderous elephant seal, became apparent.

In time with this British mercantile activity, but by no means in consort, moved that of the American sealers and whalers, including Edmund Fanning and Nathaniel Palmer, both men of great intrepidity and enterprise. They were proud of the youthful independence of their country (1776), and the "second" war of 1812-14 served to increase the spirit of rivalry between Britain and America which obscured and confused movements and discoveries in the early part of the century. While great cargoes of manageable sealskins for Canton remained the ambition of many, the cumbersome whale and the elephant seal were also hunted relentlessly. Early New England accounts record that the average yearly harpoonings of right whales over a long period exceeded ten thousand. In recent times there has been much controversy, often heated and acrimonious, about the priorities of discoveries in this era. At the time, however, many sightings of forlorn coasts under dangerous conditions of fog, swell and ice would not have been considered significant unless the areas were worth subsequent revisiting for the sake of their seal colonies, and hence the discoveries were kept secret. Logs were as sketchy and charts as fragmentary as safety allowed, but rumours and hopes were only limited by the love of adventure and the greatness of hearts.

The South Shetland Islands, ice outliers of a suspected continent, had been discovered by an Englishman, William Smith, in February 1819. In the next year Edward Bransfield, R.N., was dispatched by naval authorities to determine whether the land seen was actually insular or continental. Smith was with him as pilot. The vessel, the brig *Williams* (used in both 1819 and 1820), charted the islands for two months, and there can be little doubt that what was eventually proved to be the mainland was sighted in lat. 64° (long.

60°W.) on 30th January 1820 and named Trinity Land. Bransfield explored with an outlook and in a manner wholly in the naval and scientific tradition of Cook, a tradition which has never died and, on memorable occasions since, has inspired some of the finest expeditions.

Ten months after Bransfield's visit the American sealer Nathaniel Palmer, in his tiny sloop *Hero* (44 tons), moving independently of Pendleton's sealing fleet anchored at Livingston Island, a hundred miles to the north, saw land in the same parts. An American account of all this, published in 1833, describes also the surprise meeting between Captain Palmer and the Russian explorer Captain Fabian von Bellingshausen in the South Shetlands. Not unnaturally, Bransfield is not mentioned. Out of such accounts rose, many years later, the controversy regarding the priority of the discovery of the antarctic mainland. It all hinges on whether Bransfield really saw the mainland, which he must certainly have approached very closely, within easy sighting distance; some American historians disparage the claims made for Bransfield in favour of those of Palmer. It is rather curious that the same chroniclers support Wilkes's sightings, which, by the same standards, simply cannot be sustained. The Palmer arguments are all interesting but rather trivial when set against the great circumnavigatory voyages which dared ice so much farther south.

Bellingshausen, in his *Mirni* and *Vostok* (both names given in his honour to Russian I.G.Y. antarctic bases in 1957), made a splendid encircling voyage with the express purpose of supplementing the discoveries of Cook. He left South Georgia early in 1820 and a year later, towards the end of his polar circumnavigation, he sighted the first land definitely to be observed within the Antarctic Circle—two islands, including Alexander I Land, only separated from the Graham Land peninsula by a strait (now George VI Sound), twenty miles wide, of perennial ice-shelf (floating ice of immense thickness).

James Weddell, a retired British naval officer of spirit, has the distinction of being the first to get farther south than Cook. After sealing in the South Orkneys (discovered by the Americans Powell and Palmer in 1821), he was enabled by unusually "open" conditions to sail south in the sea which now bears his name to within nine hundred and forty-five miles of the pole, reaching lat. 74°15'S. in 34°17'W. on 22nd February 1823.

The great firm of Samuel Enderby and Sons, adventurous London shipowners, merchants, sealers, whalers and carriers upon the high seas, had commenced operations in 1785. Many of the most significant discoveries in antarctic seas were made by Enderby men, who were enjoined never to lose any opportunity of adding to Britain's maritime discoveries and renown. John Biscoe—we have living-huts at Mawson named after both Weddell and him—who circumnavigated Antarctica, annexed Graham Land for Britain and, amongst other discoveries, named Enderby Land during his voyage of 1831-32, has already been mentioned. He sailed through no less than fifty degrees of longitude inside the Antarctic Circle—at least twelve hundred miles—in the brig *Tula*, accompanied by the 50-ton cutter *Lively*. Kemp, a master mariner in the Enderbys' service, had his name added to the map east of Enderby Land for his discoveries in 1833. It is of particular interest to Australians that it was the Enderbys' fleet of whalers which not only was the first to round Cape Horn and open up much of the Southern Ocean to the enterprise of fur- and oil-seeking but also transported many convicts to Botany Bay.

Some of the vessels used by these sealer-explorers were far smaller even than those of Cook. In 1838 John Balleny sailed for Enderby in a schooner, the *Eliza Scott*, of 154 tons, with the cutter *Sabrina*, 54 tons, in attendance; he eventually nudged the pack for his fifty degrees of longitude from almost directly south of New Zealand (178°E.) to a point about in line with Esperance, Western Australia. His

farthest south was 69° at long. 170°E.; then he was forced
north-west and beyond the Circle. He made a landing at the
ice-sheathed Balleny Islands (163°E.) in 1839 (next visited,
probably, by the ANARE, under Stuart Campbell, in 1948)
and later saw what he thought looked like land in about
121°E. This was subsequently called Sabrina Land* by
Charles Enderby in honour of the gallant little cutter which
was lost in a storm with all hands.

Several other important national expeditions were undertaken during the first half of the nineteenth century. Wilkes
I have already mentioned; he made two distinguished voyages—through the South Shetlands in 1839, and for about
fifteen hundred miles somewhere off the coasts of the Australian sector of Antarctica in 1840. His little fleet was unsuitable, his crews disaffected, his season harsh and his
resulting work far from accurate, but Dr Hugh Mill's assessment of more than fifty years ago seems likely to stand:
"Considering the deplorable conditions against which he had
to contend both in the seas without and the men within his
ships, the voyage of Wilkes was one of the finest pieces of
determined effort on record." His contemporaries were two
of the world's most distinguished explorers: Captain Jules
Dumont d'Urville of the French navy, who had already
made two fine voyages round the world that carried out
valuable scientific work in biology, and Captain James Clark
Ross, with years of arctic voyaging behind him, including
the attainment of the North Magnetic Pole in 1831.

Dumont d'Urville, in command of the *Astrolabe,* had
voyaged to Australia and the Pacific Islands while seeking
news of La Pérouse. In 1838 he tried, for his country's
honour, to go farther south than James Weddell had done
fifteen years before, but he was blocked by the incalculable
pack while still north of the Circle. Having fulfilled his
commission as far as seemed humanly possible, and for good
measure named part of Graham Land for his king, Louis

* Sabrina Coast is now the accepted name.

Philippe, he rather gladly left antarctic waters. But nearly two years later, while in Australia, d'Urville heard of the movements of Wilkes and Ross and made a dash south to forestall them, if it should be possible, at the South Magnetic Pole. (This was, actually, to remain unvisited that century.) It was on this voyage, on 21st January 1840, that the Frenchman sighted the coast of the now-famous French sector, Adélie Land (named after Mme Dumont d'Urville). In a grey fog of misunderstanding no less than of weather d'Urville's *Astrolabe* and one of poor Wilkes's vessels, the *Porpoise,* passed each other a week later without ceremony. The record of the Frenchman's polar voyages was published after his death in twenty-three volumes titled, a trifle imaginatively, *Voyage au Pole Sud.*

If there is one man in the whole history of antarctic exploration who can stand beside Captain Cook, it is Ross. He had heard of d'Urville's work and had received a letter claiming extensive discoveries from Lieut. Charles Wilkes. He was obviously piqued (although at this stage he accorded Wilkes great credit), and he resolved to take an entirely different meridian to the south. This is where good fortune commenced a partnership with fine seamanship and great courage. The chosen line—170°E., where Balleny found conditions best—is, to this day, the route which may lead a ship farther south than any other. When the dauntless Roald Amundsen and his party set off on their triumphant journey to the South Pole, seventy years later, they left from almost the precise point of the farthest south of James Ross, and all Admiral Byrd's "Little Americas" were close to it.

The *Erebus,* 370 tons, under Captain Ross, and the *Terror,* 340 tons, commanded by Francis Crozier, were heavily built wooden men-o'-war, wallowing vessels but very stout and strengthened for ice like the northern whalers. They reached the edge of the pack ice on the last day of 1840. There it lay in great and small floes to the southward, with immense mysterious bergs of unknown origin standing in majesty and menace here and there, and even rising from hidden ice-strewn seas beyond the horizon. It was the expected sight of a phenomenon which had foiled or intimidated all men who had ever seen it. Sometimes it had lain infinitely tranquil, a sight beyond this world, gleaming dazzlingly, seeming too vast and level to be material but perhaps with dark pools and lanes to snatch the imagination of the watcher back to his unpredictable sea. Or, again, it had heaved sullenly and dangerously, and men faced a terrible transition from the open sea, however fearful, to the grinding edge of the unknown, jagged mills of ice in which any ship of that day risked destruction.

And, of course, it is still there beyond the outriding bergs, and the first sight of it must always astonish and awe men. I have never seen anything like it when it is calm unless it be the upper surface of a sea of sunlit clouds looked down on from a high mountain or a plane; but that is not quite right, for each of the cloud flock would need to be a cubic sheep and the upthrusting cumuli would have to be blocked in icy steps and pediments. When the edge of the pack is stormy, it is still a grey, appalling nightmare.

Five days after reaching the edge of the southern pack ice Ross and Crozier intentionally turned their vessels into it, a venture never previously undertaken. There was nothing to denote the limits of the ice-littered sea and, even in the light of his arctic experience, here was a course that demanded of Ross superlative courage and confidence. It was all brilliantly successful, for, on 10th January, the ships entered open water beyond the pack. Today the existence of this phenomenon, caused by the northerly drift in summer of the remnants of the previous year's frozen sea, is a calculated probability, but in Ross's day it could not have been foreseen. So this courageous and fortunate man sailed on towards his goal, the South Magnetic Pole.

Next day, however, an immense range of high mountains, trending south, grew strong on the horizon; it was the first

*ANARE photo: A. Campbell-Drury*

Cliffs 80-100 feet high on the edge of an ice-shelf. Such cliffs are common all round Antarctica, but the striae are seldom so marked except in areas of very heavy snowfall.

M.V. *Kista Dan*, one of the Danish vessels chartered by ANARE, in heavy seas south of Heard Island.

*ANARE photo: Phillip Law*

Icebergs in a frozen sea. Though probably over 100 feet high they are mere remnants of some great tabular berg that may have been grounded for decades, even centuries. The bulk of an iceberg below the surface is six to eight times that of the visible part.

indisputable landscape of Antarctica ever to be seen, and its splendour of alternating cliffs and glaciers has never been rivalled. Having named the Admiralty Range (its peaks were called after his naval masters) and Cape Adare, Ross continued gaining latitude, beyond any previously attained, and sighting new features along the western boundaries of his great new sea. The culminating discoveries occurred on 28th January 1841, when the explorers were confronted by a high ice-clad volcano in eruption and also found their course blocked by a huge barrier cliff of ice abutting the coast and stretching eastward beyond sight. The frustrated Ross, who had been encouraged to hope that he might sail beyond the eightieth parallel, likened the abrupt wall that sealed off the unknown to the familiar but equally uncompromising cliffs of Dover. He called the astonishing volcano, which is on Ross Island, Mount Erebus; it remains unmatched on the antarctic continent. There was no further way to be made south, so Ross steered fearlessly east, following the mysterious "barrier" for two hundred and fifty miles and establishing that the vast mass of ice was afloat in water hundreds of fathoms deep. He then returned to Hobart for the winter. The "barrier" edge was in fact the boundary of an iceberg as large as France (more than twice the area of Victoria) permanently covering half of the great gulf of the Ross Sea. It is now known as the Ross Ice Shelf; its formation will be discussed in a later chapter.

It was typical of James Ross that he returned to his enigma in the following summer, but this time, having left the Bay of Islands in New Zealand, he sailed for the pack on a course much farther east. As subsequent exploration has revealed, he met the ice-floes on the edge of an area where the disposition of winds and currents and the trend of the coasts cause an accumulation which must at times occupy half a million square miles of the Southern Ocean.

Frequently the first really calm water an expedition comes upon is in the pack, where the floes damp the movement of

c

the sea. On this voyage, however, Ross experienced one of
the most frightful storms in history, the huge swell bom-
barding the *Erebus* and *Terror* with great blocks of ice,
smashing their rudders and threatening to dash the two ships
together and to pieces. The seas were described by Ross as
"an ocean of rolling fragments of ice, hard as floating rocks
of granite". Yet the storm was weathered. The pack was
first entered on 18th December 1841 at 60°S. 146°W. The
vessels were no less than six weeks ice-encumbered, but in
that time covered more than eight hundred miles through the
floes. At one stage the audacious Ross actually had both his
vessels, under full sail, moored to a suitable floe which he
used as a battering ram. Ross must stand alone for enterprise
and courage in antarctic navigation. On another occasion
before that voyage ended, after an unavoidable collision
with the *Terror*, he backed the *Erebus* stern first in a hurricane to avoid an iceberg. He had "the maintack hauled on
board sharp aback—an expedient that perhaps had never
before been resorted to by seamen in such weather". All men
who breast the ice in modern ships should read Ross and be
comforted.

Ross came upon his "barrier" three weeks after leaving
the pack ice, and his eastward departure this time took him
to long. 161°27'W. in the highest latitude he attained—
78°11'S.—close to the end of the ice-shelf near King Edward VII Land (named by Captain Scott many years later).
He returned by his original route of the previous year
through a thickening sheet of new ice late in the season and,
after other dangers well countered, eventually he reached
the Falkland Islands. A third summer in the antarctic seas
did not add to Ross's achievements owing to the vagaries of
ice in the Weddell Sea, his chosen sector for 1843.

After Ross no one entered the open water of his sea for
more than fifty years; interest in the Antarctic lapsed while
the Arctic again sprang into focus on account of Sir John

Franklin's tragic attempt to discover a north-west passage from the Atlantic to the Pacific, across the north of Canada.

When interest again quickened it was in response not only to the age-old incentives of adventure and fame but, more than ever before, to the spur of science. From the time of James Ross to the present day (and perhaps, strange thought, since James Cook) men have lived from one expedition to the next, by word of mouth, to advise and inspire their successors and probably to give them the little personal wrinkles that have escaped all the official chronicles. Doubtless Ross himself was inspired by his father, Sir John, the arctic voyager who was born while Cook still roved the southern seas. One of Ross's surgeons was destined to be numbered amongst the greatest scientists of his century. This was Sir Joseph Hooker (1817-1911), who never failed to urge the importance to science of further antarctic exploration. He survived to see the first great scientific expeditions of the twentieth century and had close contact with their leaders, Robert Falcon Scott and Ernest Shackleton.

Before it closed the nineteenth century witnessed three significant antarctic conquests. The first circumscribed adventure itself, for there was an element of routine brought about by the magnificent nonchalance of the masters of small whaling vessels which cruised outside the pack or along the coasts of Graham Land. Many of these expeditions were Scandinavian, men and vessels that had felt the shock of the iron-hard arctic floes. To this day the movement continues; many of the same names recur—Larsen, Christensen, Andersen, Evensen, Petersen, Amundsen and other sons of the north—and many of the vessels sail out from the old ports and the fabulous fiords under the watchful eye of such vikings and veterans as old Svend Foyn. These men were fundamentally interested in what the southern waters might yield, but they were experienced explorers, and they recorded and mapped their discoveries, eventually producing their own charts of the whaling coasts. Several fine polar explorers absolute served their apprenticeship in whalers, including Dr W. S. Bruce, who sailed with a Dundee craft in 1892, and Carstens Borchgrevink, a resident of Melbourne who joined Foyn's famous expedition of 1894-5, under Kristensen in the *Antarctic*. This voyage was notable, for during its course the first landing on the antarctic mainland was made at Cape Adare.

The second conquest was a slender, almost Pyrrhic, victory over the midday darkness of the antarctic winter, and perhaps it was rather thrust upon the *Belgica's* commander and company, who nevertheless acquitted themselves more than creditably. The Belgian expedition, like several other later and larger national ventures, arose from the International Geographic Congress of 1895, held in London. It was a private scientific venture, owing its very existence to the enthusiasm of its leader, Adrien de Gerlache, who obtained a vessel of only 250 tons and barely sufficient equipment. Its work commenced in late 1897 in Tierra del Fuego and continued with the taking of valuable soundings between South America and Graham Land.

It was late in the season by the time de Gerlache had isolated the Palmer Archipelago from Graham Land and he found himself beyond the seventieth parallel at the end of February. Perhaps half intentionally, half fatalistically, and certainly against the desire of most, he let the *Belgica* be driven southwards until she was beset by ice and beyond the point of any possible return that season. It was certainly much to the advantage of the cosmopolitan company on board that it included not only the gallant and quixotic commander and the brave Captain Lecointe but a clear-eyed, imperturbable Norwegian mate called Roald Amundsen and an extraordinarily resourceful American physician, Dr Frederick Cook.

No description of shortening days and the approach of winter could fully have prepared the expedition for the misery and uncertainty, the interminable storm and darkness, of the months that followed. Ill-equipped, improperly provisioned, insufficiently lit and warmed, the *Belgica* and her company entered the loneliness and gloom of the first polar winter experienced by human beings in the southern hemisphere. Everyone became emaciated and ill; Lieutenant Danco, the geomagnetician, died. Yet meteorological and other observations were recorded and ultimately were considered of great value; they were more extensive than the purely scientific results of any previous antarctic expedition.

Some of the dramatis personae of the drift of the *Belgica* in the Bellingshausen Sea, to almost the same latitude as Captain Cook had reached on 30th January 1774, played other parts, triumphant or tragic, in future polar events. In December 1956 I was oddly moved when, into my room at ANARE's Melbourne headquarters, entered an upstanding Belgian with a special interest in the forthcoming International Geophysical Year. It was Count Gaston de Gerlache de Gomery, son of the commander of the *Belgica*.

The third special victory I mentioned came only a year after the *Belgica* had left the ice (largely owing to the resourcefulness of Frederick Cook, to whom in after years Amundsen gave unstinted credit). C. E. Borchgrevink, having obtained the necessary support of a generous patron, Sir George Newnes, found a staunch Norwegian skipper in Captain Jensen and a whaler, *The Southern Cross*, for an expedition with the object of wintering on the continent itself. After six weeks' straining against the recalcitrant pack ice in long. 165°E., a new approach more nearly in the line of Ross got them through to open water south of the ice in six hours. At Cape Adare, in mid-February 1899, Borchgrevink and his party of scientists, including L. C. Bernacchi, a Melbourne meteorologist who later sailed with Scott, set up their winter quarters. Work in geology, biology, magnetism and meteorology was undertaken and the results were of wide interest. There were no expeditions away from the coast.

So the last year of the century witnessed men in Antarctica contending with forces of gale and blizzard never previously experienced. It always takes courage to be first. Before his return in 1900 Borchgrevink followed Ross's course along the "barrier", finding that it had receded an average of thirty miles. A landing on a low ice edge was made on 19th February, and a short ski journey took Borchgrevink to a point less than seven hundred miles from the Pole. The national expeditions that followed in the new century had the benefit of Bernacchi's meteorological records in the Ross Sea area.

With the close of the nineteenth century there ended more than an era of time. Unprecedented powers over environment were very soon to change man's whole conception of his physical limitations in space and time. The great expeditions of the next two decades, those of Scott, Shackleton and Mawson, and the smaller but important journeys of Drygalski, Nordenskjöld, Bruce and Charcot, all showed many technical advances.

# 3

## THE SHAPE OF ANTARCTICA

DURING the twentieth century the pace of exploration of all kinds has been so accelerated that more is now accomplished in a year than was formerly dreamed of in a century. It was inevitable that, in the fullness of time, man should visit every part of his planet, ranging from the upper air and the summits of all mountains to the depths of its seas, and all over its surface of desert, ocean, jungle, ice-cap, and plain. His curiosity was bound to triumph over his environment, for curiosity, even concerning the nature of danger, has always been a spur to resourcefulness. In millions of years of world history a combination of the two qualities has made man the most successful animal; only his ultimate humanity, consciousness of self, remains to dare a new quality of adventure; everything else is merely quantitative, to the bounds of space.

It would be impossible and undesirable to attempt a condensation of twentieth-century antarctic exploration in this volume, for it would inevitably mean that one would never see the plateau for the ice, the great majestic ocean for the wave, or the tremendous spheres of air, the most lively element of all Antarctica, for the obscuring blizzard. The chronicles of modern expeditions must not be abbreviated; they will be read whenever circumstances create sufficient desire, and I will do little more in a summary way than, as a guide, list them at the end of the book. However, each contributes to the whole conception of Antarctica and each lives inevitably in any attempt at description. If this is your introduction to Antarctica, it will not be a credit to me if you do not seek further detail.

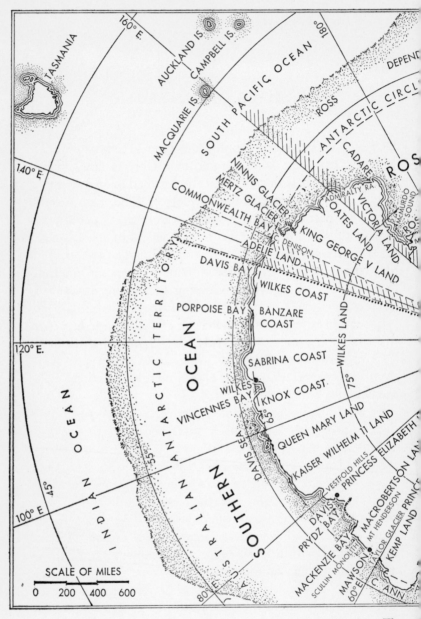

The a

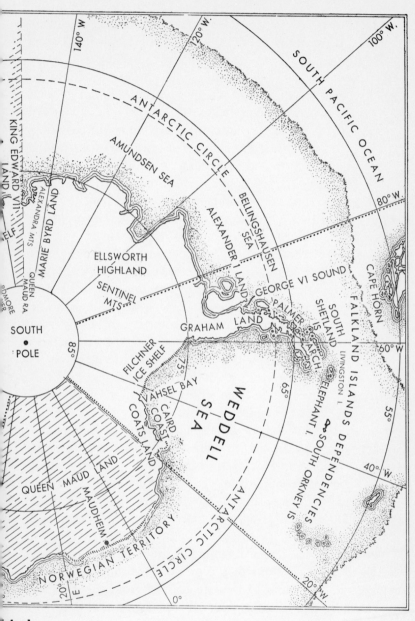

KING EDWARD VII LAND

ALEXANDRA MTS
MARIE BYRD LAND
QUEEN MAUD RA
BDMORE
ER

140° W.
120° W.
100° W.

ANTARCTIC CIRCLE

AMUNDSEN SEA

SOUTH PACIFIC OCEAN

BELLINGSHAUSEN SEA

ALEXANDER I LAND

ELLSWORTH HIGHLAND

SENTINEL MTS

GEORGE VI SOUND

80° W.

CAPE HORN

GRAHAM LAND

PALMER

SOUTH SHETLAND IS

ARCH.

LIVINGSTON I.

FALKLAND ISLANDS DEPENDENCIES

SOUTH POLE

85°

75°

FILCHNER ICE SHELF

VAHSEL BAY

CAIRD COAST

COATS LAND

WEDDELL SEA

65°

60° W.

ELEPHANT I.

SOUTH ORKNEY IS

55°

40° W.

QUEEN MAUD LAND
MAUDHEIM

NORWEGIAN TERRITORY

ANTARCTIC CIRCLE

20° E.
0°
20° W.

inland.

I have always had an intense feeling of contemporaneity in antarctic exploration, more strong than the sense in lower latitudes of sharing something with the past. It is probably accounted for by the unchanging nature of the continent, by the fact that there one may often be close to the limit of one's physical resources (though today, generally, for only a short time) and therefore very aware of every nuance of sensation, and, not least, by the extraordinary absence of decomposition in organic structure and in material generally.

In regard to the unchanging nature of Antarctica it may be said there is no other land where a coast of about fourteen thousand miles is in the same band of latitudes. Everywhere round the continent one encounters icebergs in the stormy 'fifties; everywhere in the 'sixties one may splinter the pack ice; somewhere in the 'seventies, almost all round the whole great circle, one leaves the zone of melting and ablation to the northward and enters eternal sub-freezing cold. The fierce winds everywhere round the coast stream down from the plateau, and only when they are deflected by mountains or local features, or by the movement of the earth on its axis, do they vary from a south-north direction; for this strange land has a pole from which every direction is north. At any point on the entire continent one may experience the antarctic blizzard or an atmosphere of utter silence and calm; nowhere does the ice surface differ, beyond a narrow range of colours and textures, over five million square miles. There is no other single area of the world where the ordinary senses could be so thoroughly deceived—to the extent of three thousand miles or, for that matter, three thousand years.

The second reason for a feeling of unity with the past and future is what amounts to a common fear and humility. I suppose it is possible to insulate oneself from this by buttresses and walls of safety; yet all explorers would desire to face a blizzard, to experience that strange shrinking of consciousness within concentric cores of lessening integration with environment that comes of being garbed and masked in white occlusion and bitter cold. And, in this process, one knows the limits and depths of thought in an eternal moment. It does not always need storm. I have come upon a year-old depot far out on the plateau, left by Robert Dovers or some other predecessor in common time, and found myself turning to address him. Similarly, men finding my depots on spurs of time, high and lonely in Antarctica, have forthwith dispatched radio messages to voice their companionship, though I was at home in Australia. Anyone who has sledged through crevassed areas in a cold mist far from the sea, and seen their black depths, may march humbly with Mawson as he continues eternally his homeward journey, companionless, to Cape Denison.

Inland in Antarctica chemical action is inhibited and bacteria do not survive outside their living host. The whole world spins in a deep freeze; the air and the snow are dry. Metals do not rust, wood does not rot, and flesh is incorruptible. So unchanged are the small remains of a camp that one has an uncanny entry into former circumstances; and though, eventually, time is overlain by consolidated snow, the mementoes of its passing remain intact in their strata. In a moving passage in his *Worst Journey in the World*, Apsley Cherry-Garrard speaks of Scott "coming home", borne slowly northward by the movement of the Ross Ice Shelf. Somewhere below the surface of that floating ice are the bodies of Scott and Wilson, Oates, Bowers and Edgar Evans, unchanged since the time of their deaths; but they, too, will live contemporaneously amongst antarctic travellers even when, again quoting Cherry-Garrard, Scott's "*via dolorosa* [is] a highway as practicable as Piccadilly".

We may now conveniently consider Antarctica as a whole, as it has been revealed to men sledging on foot or with dogs, moving by tractor or any other surface vehicle, flying in aeroplanes and helicopters, living through dark winters and brilliant summers. If we place ourselves outside time we may telescope the years, drawing upon the experiences of all the expeditions in any order that clarifies our vision and aids our comprehension.

The discovery of the shape of Antarctica—its actual coast-line—has been very gradual since its outside limits were defined by the circumnavigatory voyages of Cook, Bellings-hausen and Biscoe. It has not been completed in its fine de-tails yet, for the simple reason that it is exceedingly hard to know just where massive ice-sheets cease to overlie the land and become floating ice-shelves ready to fracture into bergs. Very early, of course, the stem of Antarctica, mountainous Graham Land, projecting northward towards the South American continent, was known on its western side. It is al-most surprising to realize that the eastern coast lay uncharted until Hubert Wilkins, an Australian, first used an aeroplane in Antarctica (1928). Even Sir Hubert could scarcely have foreseen the future pattern of wings over Antarctica. In the very next summer both Sir Douglas Mawson and Riiser-Larsen, the Norwegian, used planes from vessels in the In-dian Ocean sector and fixed many miles of coast. Within weeks of Wilkins's flight, Richard Byrd had planes aloft over the Ross Ice Shelf and on 29th November 1929 he flew over the Pole. They were lonely hours that these men spent in the air, before the world at large had taken to avia-tion even in their gentle homelands.

Wilkins considered that the long peninsula was actually separated from the mainland by several straits. Opposing fiords between the Weddell and Bellingshausen seas, linked by glaciers, appeared to cut the land at sea-level. It is almost amusing to recall how, in a single day, all the claims of priority made for Palmer and Bransfield were annulled. Neither had discovered Antarctica but only part of a great archipelago! One could take one's pick for a new "dis-coverer": Balleny, Wilkes, Ross. . . . However, another Australian, John Rymill, by several fine sledging journeys traversed the area in 1936-7 and restored the necessary altitudes. He also discovered George VI Sound, separating Bellingshausen's Alexander I Land from the peninsula, and thus proved very clearly that surface exploration was still necessary for detailed survey.

The two immense gulfs occupied by the Ross and Weddell seas are like jaws biting deep into the continent. Both of them long defied penetration on account of the high "barriers" of floating ice-shelf, and even the magnificent trans-polar expedition of Sir Vivian Fuchs (1958), linking the two, and the subsequent investigations of ice-depths in eastern Antarctica, leave some questions unanswered for the future. Here we must go back in time and see how Captain Scott and his party carried on from Ross beyond his "barrier" and shaped the south-west limits of the Ross Sea to 82°17'S. (about five hundred and thirty miles from the Pole).

The second skirting of the "barrier" after its discovery by Ross was accomplished, and, on 30th January 1902, the rock faces of the Alexandra Mountains of King Edward VII Land at its eastern extremity provided ocular evidence of land whose existence below the rising ice was already certain. After turning back Robert Scott went up in a balloon, becoming, in his own words, "the first aëronaut to make an ascent in the Antarctic Regions". He did not see much apart from great undulations, deceptive clouds that might have betokened land, and the tiny sledge of Armitage and Bernacchi (who had been at that same place with Borchgrevink), but, had he looked "into the seeds of time", he might have seen spread before him his great reward, transcending even the bitterness of his final journey.

He would have watched open below him a great rift in the ice-shelf as huge bergs slowly drifted away, and seen the whales disporting there when Ernest Shackleton—six future years away—bestowed the obvious name on the calm water. He would doubtless have seen, amongst Shackleton's grand company, my honoured friends John King Davis and Sir Douglas Mawson, young men with great futures. In this

Bay of Whales he would have watched Roald Amundsen
(of *Belgica* fame), his fine, relentless rival, setting up his
base, Framheim, for his superb race to the South Pole.
Amazed, he might have descried members of Shirase's Jap-
anese expedition of 1912 and, with a light in his eye, he
might have greeted his first successors in the air over the
Bay of Whales as they came in to found Little America,
after being towed through the pack by the mighty *Larsen*,
a 17,000-ton whaling factory ship, in December 1928. They
brought with them only three little monoplanes, under
Richard Byrd, already famous for his north polar flight of
1926; but how Scott would have thrilled to see them being
towed by tractor and dog teams to the site of the new station;
and how precisely, in naval fashion, would he have saluted
Byrd, Balchen, Parker and Smith when on 15th January
1929 they skimmed past his swaying basket, airborne on
wings for the first time over the Ross Sea.

Fascinated he might have watched Ellsworth and Hollick-
Kenyon land after their great continental flight from Graham Land between 21st November and 5th December 1935,
during which they had risen over mountains (the Sentinel
Mountains) thirteen thousand feet high. Then there would
have grown before Scott's incredulous eyes, as he stared
through sixty years, all of Admiral Byrd's five bases; his
surface vessels and submarines, thousands of men, hundreds
of buildings, his shuddering tractors and huge aeroplanes,
jet-assisted, screaming over the ice. And, between these
mighty operations, which led to the photo-mapping of prac-
tically the whole coast of Antarctica, Scott would have
watched the Bay of Whales itself—his old Balloon Bight—
disappear as square miles of table-topped bergs drifted away
from the inexorable pressure of the Ross Ice Shelf.

After his balloon ascent Scott returned to the western end
of the shelf before setting up his winter quarters. In the
next spring he sledged over the floating ice along the coast
of Victoria Land to his record south latitude of 82°17'S. for

the expedition, reached on 30th December 1902. He and his men made other journeys over the ice in this and the following season, including the first great probe inland, westwards, at about 78°S., for about two hundred miles.

There are many expeditions which should receive credit for the delineating of Antarctica on our maps and—praise be!—there are many opportunities still to mark the tell-tale hinge crevasses where ice-shelves meet the indisputable land-based ice. We have seen something of the Ross Sea. What of the opposing gulf and the ice-shelf of the Weddell Sea? If the former is the memorial of Ross and Scott, the glory of the latter is shared with Weddell by Bruce (1904), Filchner (1912) and Shackleton (1915-16). Shackleton not only had been with Scott on Scott's first expedition but, on his own account, in the summer of 1908-9, had gone to within ninety-seven miles of the South Pole. For his next expedition, in 1914, he planned a trans-polar journey. Amundsen and Scott had reached the South Pole on 14th December 1911 and 18th January 1912 respectively, and Scott and his companions had died during the return journey, on the Ross Ice Shelf.

Shackleton spent the first two years of the 1914-18 war ignorant of what was happening in Europe; in the Weddell Sea they were spent in one of the most gallant struggles between man and the rest of nature that has ever occurred in history, while, on the other side of Antarctica, depots were laid to the foot of the Beardmore Glacier down which Shackleton hoped to descend. The sum of all the movements contained triumph and disaster and such complexities that even the several volumes written by those who were there, including Shackleton's *South*, cannot entirely tell the story. The *Endurance* became icebound in the Weddell Sea in about 75°S. on 18th January 1915, near the newly discovered Caird Coast of Bruce's Coats Land and close to Filchner's Vahsel Bay. In this region, more than forty years later, a cluster of I.G.Y. bases was set up by the nations and, in time,

Shackleton's plan was inevitably fulfilled by Sir Vivian Fuchs, with Sir Edmund Hillary and his New Zealanders providing support from the Ross Sea, the Americans assisting at the Pole, and mechanics and electronics, as they stood in 1958, helping all the way.

The drift of the *Endurance*, until she was crushed and, in November 1915, swallowed by the pressure ice, the subsequent five months while the party was carried on ice-floes, the eventual launching of small boats and the gaining of Elephant Island, are part of a modern odyssey without parallel, culminating in the boat journey to South Georgia and the crossing of that island to obtain assistance. Most of Shackleton's company remained on Elephant Island with Frank Wild, living under upturned boats until rescue came from Chile after twenty-two months.

Meanwhile the Ross Sea party had been beset by tragedy, danger and discomfort, and their vessel, the *Aurora*, had broken loose in a hurricane from her moorings in McMurdo Sound (at about midnight on 6th May 1915). It was 10th January 1917 before they learned on shore what had happened to the *Aurora* and her company under Captain Stenhouse. With a great deal of the expedition's gear and supplies on board, she had drifted into the pack before a southerly blizzard and been quite unable to regain her anchorage near Cape Evans, on Ross Island. Fortunately the resourcefulness and courage of Stenhouse brought the *Aurora* safely through the winter pack ice to New Zealand.

The *Aurora* had been purchased by Shackleton from Douglas Mawson, whose skipper and second-in-command, Captain John King Davis, had done remarkable work along the coasts of the Australian sector during the years 1911-14 —while Mawson was conducting one of the most generally successful antarctic expeditions that had ever taken place. When the *Aurora* again sailed south in the summer after her historic drift under Stenhouse, it was under her old

*ANARE photo: John Béchervaise*
The antarctic coast in winter: frozen sea, ice-cliffs and rocky islands.

Scene in the Prince Charles Mountains.

*ANARE photo: M. Fisher*

MASSON RANGE · PLATEAU HERE 3000 ft ABOVE SEA · DAVID RANGE

2000 ft

MOUNT HENDERSON

CREVASSES

FLOW-LINES IN ICE

400 ft

ICE CLIFFS 80-100 ft HIGH

CREVASSED ICE-DOME COVERING ROCK

MAWSON

HORSE-SHOE HARBOUR

SEA-ICE

*ANARE photo: R.A.A.F.*

The coast and plateau near Mawson, photographed from 10,000 feet. Frozen sea occupies the lower right-hand third of the picture, land the remainder. The coast, with ice-cliffs 80-120 feet high, runs diagonally from the bottom left-hand corner. Halfway along the coast is the well-named Horseshoe Harbour, with an arm of rock on either side; the huts of Mawson (not visible) are at the top of the left rocky arm. In the background are Mt Henderson (left), the Masson Range (centre) and the David Range (right). Running from the mountains to the sea are the flow lines of the ice. Midway between Horseshoe Harbour and the left edge of the page is a large crevassed ice-dome, formed over rock. On the horizon the plateau is some 4500 feet above sea-level, just behind Mawson 400 feet.

skipper, Captain Davis, with Shackleton, straight from South America, to direct any necessary land operations.

Such is the complex story of antarctic seas and coasts; it is continued whenever a vessel thrusts aside the floes, whenever a plane determines the limits of hidden land or sea, or when members of a sledging party set up their instruments to find precisely where on earth they are. Since the establishment of Australia's first permanent mainland base, so aptly named Mawson, Phillip Law, his Danish skippers, and a number of fortunate Australians have filled in much of the necessary detail on existing charts.

# 4

# WORLD OF ICE

SCOTT, Shackleton, Mawson and Amundsen and their teams are the men who revealed the nature of Antarctica. They penetrated beyond the coastal frontiers and dared hazards which, however great they may remain objectively, for them held the added primary chill of being unknown. There is no danger but that measured by human standards. Until the unknown is illumined, the quality and quantity of its perils may be imagined only and are therefore infinite. Even to-day there is an entirely different atmosphere about journeying in Antarctica the moment one enters untraversed territory.

In the days of the great quartet whose names open this chapter Antarctica was still the Unshapen Land, a more fearful prospect than that before Perseus, and the "grey sisters" of cold, blizzard and crevasse, such as Antarctica held, had never been encountered or estimated. These men learned how they might foil weather and ice, and they recorded everything so that future explorers would never be at their disadvantage.

Mawson, the Australian, probably encountered conditions more rigorous than any ever previously experienced, and his account, *The Home of the Blizzard,* should be read by everyone interested in Antarctica, along with the chronicles of Scott and Shackleton. It was basically the fine work of Sir Douglas Mawson and his teams in King George V, Adélie and Queen Mary lands in 1911-14 (the A.A.E.—Australasian Antarctic Expedition) and in further areas of discovery in 1929-31 (the B.A.N.Z.A.R.E.—British-Australian-New Zealand Antarctic Research Expedition) that led to the creation of Australian Antarctic Territory in 1933, when Britain granted to Australia her own well-founded claims to the area between long. 45°E. and long. 160°E., except for the narrow French sector of Adélie Land.

The great expeditions, the shorter probes from bases set up by various nations either on the coast or inland, and the continent's extensive aerial inspection have all taken place within the twentieth century. Individual ambitions and achievements have differed widely and triumphs have sometimes been blended with tragedy. Details of many operations are extraordinarily complex, and, as in the previous chapter, we shall here consider the whole to which they have all contributed, rather than attempt a chronological survey, which would necessarily be repetitive, if not confusing. First, in this chapter, we shall examine the form of the antarctic continent within the coastal bounds we have already drawn and discussed.

Early in the century it became convenient among geographers to refer to East and West Antarctica because of differences that, with successive expeditions, had steadily become more obvious, the dividing line being approximately the 0°-180° compound meridian of Greenwich and the International Date Line. Between the two divisions lie the great indentations of the Ross and Weddell seas and a transcontinental lowland far below the ice virtually linking, in its depths, the Pacific and Atlantic oceans. Geological studies by Edgeworth David and R. E. Priestley revealed that the high mountains first sighted by Ross in 1841, walling the western side of his sea, were uplifted as a great horst between parallel faults (conceivably running right across Antarctica), raising ancient strata of sediments thousands of feet thick and immense sheets or sills of volcanic rocks to heights exceeding thirteen thousand feet above sea-level. Further peaks of up to fifteen thousand feet have since been surveyed. Beyond these mountains, through which Shackleton (1908-9) and Scott (1911-12) toiled by way of the Beardmore Glacier, and through which each of their successors right down to Fuchs and Hillary (1958) has had to find a passage by some glacial valley, lay East Antarctica, a huge, laterally inflexible shield of granite against which the world-forming forces of the Pacific area thrust themselves.

The general theory, as promulgated by Griffith Taylor (who had been with Scott, 1910-11), would link the systems of young fold mountains of New Zealand, through those of West Antarctica and the Graham Land peninsula, with the Andes, by way of a loop taking in South Georgia. It suggests a downfold or geosyncline, probably largely filled with ice and sagging under its enormous weight, right across Antarctica. This might possess a common origin with the depression of the Tasman Sea. The structure of Antarctica, by this hypothesis, would have many similarities, as Griffith Taylor suggests, with that of Australia, the granite shield of Western Australia and the horsts of the south-eastern highlands corresponding, respectively, to East Antarctica and the ranges of Victoria Land.

In 1957, at Byrd, the American research station on the eightieth parallel, between the Ross and Weddell seas, an ice-depth of ten thousand feet was sounded at an altitude of five thousand feet above sea-level. Subsequent American traversing with seismic sounding apparatus has revealed an astonishing continuation of such great depths of ice and, of course, of their rock foundations. By the end of the 1958-9 summer season it was established that the immense volume of ice discovered at Byrd filled a broad trough, averaging about three hundred and fifty miles in width, linking the beds of the Ross and Bellingshausen seas. Furthermore, newly discovered extensions of the Filchner Ice Shelf, south of the Weddell Sea, approach this trough so closely that the peninsula of Graham Land is now known to be attenuated far southwards to form a narrow barrier, well beyond 80°S., separating the sea-beds, virtually, of the Pacific and Atlantic oceans. There are some who believe that a narrow trench through this barrier, detaching Graham Land from East Antarctica, still remains to be discovered.

Obvious in many parts of the coast, the foundations of East Antarctica are granites and gneisses, schists and other ancient (pre-Cambrian) rocks metamorphosed by pressure and heat. Overlying them, in many areas, are sediments including limestones and the coal-bearing Beacon sandstones (named by Ferrar, 1907), themselves probably in parts covered by later plutonic intrusions. In some of the coastal regions of East Antarctica the granites have been laid bare by ice action, and geologists have travelled hundreds of miles from the sea before they discovered sedimentary rocks. This is typically so of the mountainous areas inland from Mawson (MacRobertson Land) and Maudheim (Queen Maud Land). It has generally become apparent that considerable mountain ranges project above the ice to altitudes of thirteen thousand feet or more at wide intervals in East Antarctica.

In West Antarctica, almost islanded by recent American ice soundings, an entirely different geological structure is apparent. There are few areas revealing pre-Cambrian rocks and even the older fossil-bearing strata are rare, but deposits of the middle and later periods (Triassic down to Pliocene) are found over wide, frequently extensively folded, mountain regions. The younger rocks are rich in fossils, providing absolute evidence of a vastly different climate in past time, with plants that bore many close resemblances to those of both temperate and tropical lands today. There has also been a good deal of recent volcanic activity in West Antarctica.

One of the most fascinating theories concerning Antarctica was first proposed by Eduard Suess (1831-1914), a celebrated Austrian geologist, in his great work, *The Face of the Earth* (1885). His view, which has commanded attention ever since and which has been accepted, with or without modification, by a number of leading geologists, was that Antarctica once formed part of a super-continent which he called Gondwanaland (after an area in central India). This great

landmass would have contained South America, Africa, India
and Australia. According to the theory the southern continents drifted apart, their deep foundations in the semi-fluid
magma of a substratum of the earth's crust. It is, in fact,
not difficult to arrange the continents as though they had
been huge fragments of a mighty jigsaw puzzle, or even to
reconcile their arrangement with crustal folding as apparent
today. If the drift theory is proved it will certainly assist
greatly in an assessment of Antarctica's possible mineral resources.

There are other learned opinions which favour the subsidence of lands now inundated by ocean, or the existence
from time to time in geological history, of bridges between
the continents. All theories seek to explain the great changes
that have obviously taken place in the climate of Antarctica,
and some endeavour to show how similar plant species probably migrated between allied or bridged landmasses. The
most direct evidence, other than the existing gross structure,
is, of course, in the similarity of rocks along coasts which
may once have been contiguous. Wegener, the German scientist, in 1922 postulated a continent containing all the land
surfaces of the world. All the hypothetical reconstructions
either of Gondwanaland or in accordance with the Wege-
nerian theory have placed the shields of Western Australia
and East Antarctica in contact; there is certainly a marked
resemblance between the rocks present along both coasts.

The drift theory buttresses conveniently the fact of a
great climatic change, but there are numerous anomalies to
hinder the uncritical acceptance of any single existing statement.

However, the one illimitable element is time. Movements
of the order of an inch a year, almost imperceptible in the
human scale, would raise altitudes twice as high as Everest
in less than a million years. That movements do occur, especially in the levels of ice and sea, may be seen in many parts
of the coast of Antarctica where wave-cut terraces have risen,

relative to our present sea-level, by many feet. Such a phenomenon is very clearly visible on Welch Island, quite close to Mawson. (Welch Island was a favourite walk or sledging trip in early summer when I was at Mawson, to hunt seals for the dogs or to observe the penguins.)

During his arctic voyage of 1610-11 Henry Hudson made a distinctive cut in the rock where it rose out of the ice of the bay named after him. That mark has risen at an average rate of almost two inches annually during the last three hundred years, on account of the slow decrease in the burden of ice resting on the north of Canada. There is no doubt that in Antarctica, too, the ice-level has greatly fallen, in some areas by hundreds of feet. On the summits of coastal mountains near Mawson there is evidence of glacial erratics—boulders moved from far away to their present position by the agency of ice.

We may state with certainty, from the evidence of fossil plants, including the vast seams of coal thousands of miles long in Victoria Land, that ice gradually overwhelmed a formerly fertile continent. The geological age or ages in which this occurred are not known precisely, nor are the causes. It might have been the outcome of the supposed Permian drift of continents. Antarctica may have been edged into the polar regions, displacing other landmasses now temperate or tropical which show evidence of past glaciation in ice-scored rocks and U-shaped valleys. However, there is a problem here, at present unresolved, in that no antarctic evidence exists of such ancient glacierization; on the contrary, the coal seams are of Permian period and great quantities of fossils of sub-tropical plants, of Jurassic period, exist in West Antarctica.

One may imagine how, in the slow passage of time, gradually the snows of winter ceased to melt on the mountains; how they crept down the slopes and at length lay through the summers, even in the valleys. Then, by degrees, many kinds of animals must, with the plant life, have perished or

adapted themselves to the infinitely slow changes. This evolution in time is very difficult for our minds to comprehend.
We must think of the period, say, since Julius Caesar landed
in Britain—two thousand years—as a brief instant in geological time. Inexorably, if our theory is correct, all life must
have moved towards the coasts of Antarctica and ultimately
taken to the sea, seals and penguins evolving limbs from the
legs and wings of their land and air ancestors to swim and fly
through water. Then the frozen deposits of successive centuries must finally have filled the valleys and overtopped
the mountains, becoming more and more compressed under
their own weight until they became solid ice.

Such ice is formed by a slow continuous process as the air
is forced to the surface; in the constantly sub-freezing climate of the antarctic plateau—where there is virtually no
surface melting such as occurs in the snowfields in gentler
latitudes, causing water to percolate through the drifts—
always a certain amount of air remains trapped and compressed. A quantitative estimation of this and of the degree
of its compression leads to a reckoning of the age of ice
samples. Over a period of years the average annual accumulation of crystalline snow or *névé* may be measured against
stakes planted in selected areas. As a rule it amounts to a
few inches only, for most of the snow, dry and non-adhesive
owing to the intense cold, is blown northward out to sea, or
until it forms lee drifts in mountainous regions. Sometimes,
in the walls of a pit dug in the *névé*, it is possible to discern
faint seasonal striae where the finer weather of summer,
when there is little precipitation but an almost daily movement of scurrying drift, polishes a surface which is buried
in darker days. So, on the plateau, one may pass down
through history, penetrating snows that fell in former years.
A core lifted by an ice-drill may bring to the eye the precipitation of the year that Captain Cook circumnavigated the
pack ice and commenced our history of the far south. You

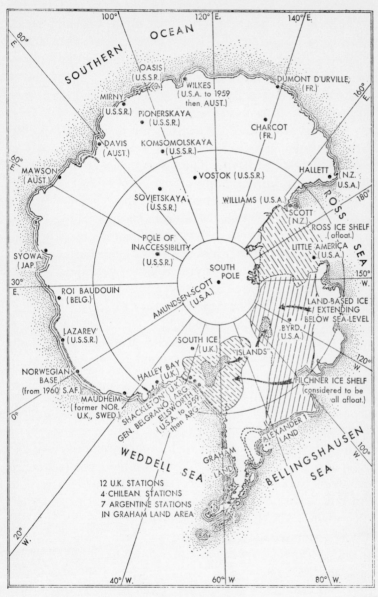

The scientific bases of the International Geophysical Year
and subsequent years.

could melt ice-crystals for your evening drink that had lain frozen since the time of Christ.

In recent years accurate depth determinations have been made possible by the process, already mentioned, known as seismic sounding. In this the time taken for shock waves (artificially induced by controlled explosions) to travel through the ice is measured. Since the waves travel at a known rate, depending on density, the depth can be calculated. I have mentioned one result obtained in this way at the U.S. station Byrd. The Norwegian-British-Swedish Expedition to Queen Maud Land (1949-52) made long seismic traverses of the plateau to and about mountains hundreds of miles from their Maudheim base, revealing for the first time, with great accuracy, the topography of the land beneath the ice and the thickness of its over-burden. Extraordinary and unexpected variations were found, proving that whole mountain ranges and depressions far below sea-level lay beneath the ice. The Americans have recently proved that even the South Pole, long thought to be high on account of underlying rock, actually must be produced downwards through something over nine thousand feet of *névé* and ice to stand on a rock base.

The Russians, on an I.G.Y. seismic programme, traversed the ice from their coastal station at Mirny for two hundred and fifty miles to Pionerskaya during 1957, and at no place sounded bed-rock above sea-level. French scientists have discovered depressions in Adélie Land two thousand feet below sea-level. Fuchs's soundings between the Weddell Sea and the Pole have not revealed such depths, but the coincident Australian (ANARE) expedition of some eight hundred miles, under Mather, southward and back along the sixty-second meridian, showed ice depths down to eight and a half thousand feet and several sub-nevean mountain ranges five thousand feet below the surface. Even before it was firmly established that there had been a considerable downward displacement of the earth's crust below the antarctic ice, it was reckoned that the quantity of water immobilized in the continent today could raise the level of all oceans by seventy to ninety feet, drowning many of the world's greatest cities. A recent estimate more than doubles these figures. Fortunately such changes appear to take place over a period measurable only in terms of geological time.

The surface of the planet would present a very different appearance, coastlines would be much longer, and many ancient land bridges would still exist were it not for the plastic nature of ice. Under its tremendous pressure, the central ice mass expands laterally as well as depressing the rock beneath. This gravitational force in effect causes radial coastward movements over all Antarctica, and when the ice-sheets overflow the edge of the land and float on the sea they form ice-shelves and, as they become detached, tabular icebergs. Frequently, especially from the air, immense crevassed glaciers are seen, vast slow-moving streams which, on the surface, would be scarcely comprehensible as such. When mountains deflect the flow it is often possible to see patterns in unusual moraines of rock fragments carried on the surface. Far inland, where the cold is most intense, quite small particles of rock remain on the surface for countless years, but in coastal regions, where considerable surface melting takes place in summer and where stones become warmer, the smaller fragments sink below the ice surface and, at a distance from the peaks, only the great monoliths remain above the ice moving seawards, in an extraordinary linear procession. The rate of movement of the surface varies, of course, with slope, distance from the sea, depth, nature of the underlying terrain, obstructions and temperature. It may be measured by taking a series of sights periodically with a theodolite between a mark set up on the ice and some fixed outcrop, a mountain peak or a nunatak.* The Ross Ice Shelf appears to be being pushed northward at the rate of four feet per

---

* Nunatak: a rocky crag or small mountain projecting from and surrounded by a glacier or ice-sheet.

day at its "barrier" edge. The plateau ice two thousand feet above Mawson was determined by Crohn (1955) to be advancing, on the average, only about one and a half inches daily. At this rate, rocks falling from Mount Henderson, ten miles south of Mawson, would take more than a thousand years to reach their inevitable destination at the edge of the sea.

Were it not that the bergs calved from the polar glaciers and ice-fronts complete the great ice-cycle and eventually replenish the surrounding oceans, these oceans would by now probably be disconnected inland seas, and the whole balance of the earth would be disturbed!

It should be noted, as is quickly brought to the attention of the antarctic traveller, that, although ice is plastic in its behaviour under great pressure, it is not fluid, and it may be too brittle not to fracture in conforming to the stresses imposed upon it by gravity and the underlying rock or the deflecting pinnacles of mountains that stand above its surface. The cracks and fissures so caused may vary in width from almost nothing up to dozens of yards and their depths may range to hundreds of feet, an absolute limit probably being reached where the pressure overcomes the ice's qualities of hardness and resistance to deformation. These cracks or crevasses make travelling on the surface difficult and, if they are covered by thin superficial layers of snow or *névé*, dangerous.

Men of all expeditions exploring the plateau become familiar with and wary of crevasses. Near the coast they are often very common owing to the close gravitational pull of the ice-cliffs, but they are then generally more easily visible, since they occur in the area of ablation, where surface snow is either blown off the old basic blue ice that has moved north from far inland, or melted away under the strong summer sun and by the ameliorating effect of relatively warm open water close at hand. The coastal ablation zone varies with season and latitude, of course, but, as a rule, not many miles inland upon the plateau, which generally rises steeply to some thousands of feet, one reaches its limits. Farther south, always, the air and ice temperatures are well below freezing, and even the radiant heat of the sun cannot affect the surface. On the white *névé*, naturally, most of the light and heat is reflected back into the atmosphere and not absorbed; even where darker mountains project, well inland, rock temperatures, affected by radiant heat or the ambient air, still remain below freezing and no wastage by melting takes place.

Crevasses are generally bridged wholly or partly by drift snow and *névé*. There is frequently a visible difference of texture between the bridge and its margins and often a variation in tone, the bridge being lighter in colour (especially in coastal regions). A further clue to the presence of crevasses, quite common in warmer climates, is a slumping or dipping of the bridges, which become stronger in their lower central mass than at the sides, owing to progressive subsidence and consequent filling by blown drift. For this reason, the edges, where a direct break-through is likely, are avoided if possible.

At all times, naturally, the weights of men and vehicles are distributed as widely as possible. Men travel on skis and roped together, or on sledges and vehicles with caterpillar tracks. Dogs are harnessed in a "fan" formation, so that if one should break through he will not pull the others in after him. With very few exceptions vehicles, such as sno-cats and weasels, do not press as heavily over a unit area as the human foot, so that, provided the crevasse bridge *as a whole* stands, the passage of a heavy vehicle or sledge may be considerably safer than the crossing of a man on foot. This fact was demonstrated tragically on 14th December 1912, during Sir Douglas Mawson's great dog-sledging journey across King George V Land, between Adélie Land and Ross's Admiralty Range. Lieut. B. E. S. Ninnis was travelling behind Mawson and Dr Xavier Mertz, each man with his sledge and dogs. Mawson and Mertz rode their sledges over *névé* in which were the very faint indications of a crevasse

("It was but one of many hundred similar ones we had crossed and had no specially dangerous appearance. . . ."— Mawson). Ninnis walked by his sledge, although he turned his team to cross the area at right angles—the safest way. He and his team and sledge suddenly broke through and disappeared for ever.

Mawson wrote: "The explanation appeared to be that Ninnis had walked by the side of his sledge, whereas I had crossed it sitting on the sledge. The whole weight of a man's body bearing on his foot is a formidable load and no doubt was sufficient to smash the arch of the roof."

Crevassing is, on the whole, much more static in Antarctica than it is in its better-known occurrence on steep mountain glaciers, but it follows a similar kind of time sequence, infinitely retarded. As the ice moves beyond the cause of its fracture, the surface gradually heals, but further crevasses open behind in the same region relative to the cause.

# 5

# THE ELEMENTS OF ANTARCTICA

So far, we have chiefly considered those aspects of Antarctica which, in man's chronology, change very slowly. Now we must think of the seasonal and cyclic changes that are so pronounced in the polar regions, and the elements of the storms and calms that still defy complete analysis and prediction. The less predictable factors of any environment are the ones that constitute its dangers for man and even beast; they also provide many of the most profitable fields for scientific study by offering the widest range of facets of any particular phenomenon. Frequently, too, they appeal to man's senses as being most impressive and memorable.

One of the most extraordinary contrasts to be discovered over the whole surface of our globe is the difference between the polar regions of the two hemispheres. The North Pole centres a great sea almost completely surrounded by continents. It will be noticed that the most continuous land latitude of all is close to the Arctic Circle, running through Iceland, Norway, Siberia, Alaska, northern Canada and Greenland. The South Pole, on the contrary, even in summer, is nearly a thousand miles from the nearest open ocean, and the Antarctic Circle is surrounded by the only continuous oceanic latitudes that exist anywhere in the world. Here all the great oceans commingle in circum-polar loneliness, their monotony broken only by disintegrating icebergs and a few desolate islands. The great average altitude of Antarctica, at least six thousand feet, is another point of contrast between the two regions.

On the other hand, the earth's polar latitudes have many common qualities, being both equidistant, and as far as possible, from the tropics. They therefore always receive the sun's rays more obliquely and consequently by a longer path through the earth's atmosphere than do lower latitudes. This is the fundamental reason for their being cold. But the Antarctic is a great deal colder than the Arctic. And the explanation is that the southern continent fulfils more adequately than anywhere else on earth the three conditions of frigid climate—firstly, high latitude (the highest of any landmass); secondly, high altitude (it is the most elevated of all continents and from it re-radiation of the sun's rays is as considerable as possible on account of its excellent reflecting surface and the rarity of the air); and thirdly, distance from the moderating effects of the sea. Except for the narrow coastal fringe, there is no part of the antarctic continent where the air temperature ever rises above freezing. The mean annual temperatures are the lowest on earth. By comparison, the Arctic is mild; in summer it may be hot, humid and mosquito-ridden. Although the inland winter temperatures of Siberia may fall very low, the summer heat in the same place allows prolific plant and animal life.

During the International Geophysical Year, in several parts of inland Antarctica, scientific stations, including the Amundsen-Scott Base at the South Pole and the Russian Vostok, recorded temperatures below —100°F. (132°F. below freezing). It had previously been calculated that temperatures much below this would not occur anywhere on the surface of the earth. The Australian base at Mawson, although only sixty-seven degrees south of the Equator, experiences a mean annual temperature of about +7°F. (25°F. below freezing), while—for the sake of comparison with the northern hemisphere—Spitzbergen, in lat. 80°N., has a yearly average ten degrees warmer (17°F.). It is not difficult to discover the mean annual temperature anywhere on the plateau. Summer and winter temperatures vary most near the surface, but with depth the variation becomes less, since the lower *névé* is shielded to an increasing extent from both

*ANARE photo: W. R. J. Dingle*

Young bull elephant seal amongst the ice-floes, Vestfold Hills coast. The Vestfolds are one of the few large ice-free areas on the continent, which may explain why elephant seals—usually sub-antarctic—come there

Weddell seal mother and young. The young are born in summer on the still frozen surface of the sea.

*ANARE photo: W. R. J. Dingle*

*ANARE photo: John Béchervaise*
Emperor penguins on discoloured ice at the Taylor Glacier rookery. Many have small chicks balanced on their feet.

Adélie penguins on an island off MacRobertson Land. Note the chick emerging from the egg in a nest of stones gathered and re-gathered over the centuries.
*ANARE photo: W. R. J. Dingle*

seasonal extremes. At about twelve metres the *névé* holds the approximate mean between the two. About one hundred miles south of Mawson readings at this depth give a result of —20°F., which is the same approximately as the mean annual temperature on the surface. The minimum on the surface here might be between thirty-five and forty-five degrees lower. Scott's lowest temperature on his polar journey was —46°F., on 10th March 1912, on the Ross Ice Shelf, not long before his death.

Cold is only one element of weather. By itself, even at temperatures well below zero Fahrenheit, it does not constitute a factor of any great discomfort to human beings, for the warm layer of air generated near the skin is not disturbed without wind. If the sun is shining, the flesh absorbs and re-radiates heat of a kind that warms the air in immediate contact with the skin. If this is not disturbed, one may feel pleasantly warm and even be tempted to sunbathe at temperatures many degrees below freezing. It is inanimate substances that best indicate low temperatures in still air. At —30°F. a candle leaves a little cylindrical lantern of lacy wax round half the flame; butter splinters like a stone; tepid water thrown out of doors freezes as it touches the rock or ice and forms heaps; fish drawn through a hole in the ice freeze solid and are quite brittle in a few seconds after reaching the air; a seal carcass must be sawn with a cross-cut into huge cutlets of dog-food, and the little husky pups come over, if they are allowed, to lick up the sawdust. The cutlets must be split with an axe, precisely like sections of a tree-trunk. Metals cause painful frost-burns if they are handled at these temperatures. Mercury, of course, freezes into a solid, malleable metal at —39°F. At the same temperature tin tends to disintegrate into small granules and many metals become very brittle. For most of the year, even at coastal stations like Mawson, all water required for domestic purposes is quarried from a convenient drift or glacier face and left in heaps from which it may be taken indoors for melt-

E

ing. Even the salt sea is frozen to a depth of several feet for distances of a hundred miles or more along some antarctic coasts for nine or ten months of the year—before the short midsummer weeks when it breaks out as pack ice.

Unless a person has lived through the seasons within the astronomical limits of a polar Circle and experienced not only the midnight sun and the midday darkness but the slow transition of one to the other, his appreciation of some aspects is likely to be academic. As the axis of the hemisphere changes its angle to the sun from a maximum of $113\frac{1}{2}$ degrees, when all areas within the Circle are sunlit, to its opposite extreme of inclination ($66\frac{1}{2}$ degrees), when no part of the same area has any direct sun at all (being screened by the curvature of the earth), any day is likely to provide a quality of skylight and colour unmatched in lower latitudes. Tropical sunsets and dawns are always swift and sometimes violent of colour; in polar regions they may endure for hours in a strange tranquillity, so that it almost seems as though time itself were arrested. Often, while an apricot flush of distant day still lingers on the horizon, the aurora will pulsate in the south; the effect is often one of quite unearthly beauty.

Between the equinoxes (approximately from 21st September to 21st March) the sun never sets at the South Pole; it remains just swinging round the sky, first in circles of increasing altitude until the maximum ($23\frac{1}{2}$ degrees) is reached on midsummer day; then at decreasing altitudes until it again slides round the horizon in March and slowly continues as a daylong sunset, finally dropping below the horizon until only the faintest midwinter flush is left in June to encircle the dark disc of the visible world. The strictly polar phenomena are unique, but the seasons of the two hemispheres of course differ in time by six months.

Nearer the antarctic coast, with latitude decreasing, the period of continuous midsummer sunlight becomes less and less until, a little northwards of the Antarctic Circle, there is no day when the sun actually shines through midnight. However, anywhere near or within the Circle the summer days are long and the twilight either before or after the sun's actual appearance is wonderfully protracted. All night at Mawson, for about three months, the flush of the sun is always visible somewhere in the sky, burnishing icebergs far out at sea or resting gloriously on some distant peak or glacier along the coast. It is, of course, easy to calculate the midday altitude of the sun (its elevation in degrees above the horizon) for any locality on any day by computing a resultant angle* from the latitude and the sun's declination (obtainable from a Nautical Almanac).

The continuing sunlight of the polar summer does more than merely mathematically balance the effects of the winter darkness. The sun's altitude and prolonged presence in the sky allow a greater intensity of warming in air, ice, sea and rock and the occurrence of both stable conditions and consequent effects over seasonal periods. The intense winter cold (absence of sun) which permits the sea to freeze is offset by the continuous heating which disintegrates the ice in summer. But the tilt of the earth is responsible for seasonal changes in all latitudes. Without these it is probable that the polar ice-caps, if they existed, would be much restricted; life on the Equator, on the other hand, might be unendurable. Days would always be the same length all over the world and there would be little variation in weather from one year's end to another; latitude would be the only determinant of change.

It might be inferred that the solar relations of this planet, constant from year to year, should do no more than balance their seasonal effects. This is not strictly so, since an accumulation of winter snow, with a white radiating surface, will tend to keep an area cooler than, for instance, a rock surface.

---

* Sun's meridian altitude $= 90° -$ (latitude $\pm$ declination). Take the difference of latitude and declination if they are both north or both south; otherwise obtain their sum.

Thus there is an argument for the persistence of snowfields once, for any reason, a season of unusual precipitation occurs. At present, all over the world, it seems that glaciers and ice-caps are receding. Long-term cycles have, according to geological evidence, occurred in the past, and this recession may be part of such a one; though the effects may be evaluated, the causes remain unknown. It should, however, be appreciated that the snow of intensely cold conditions is finer, lighter and drier than that of relatively warmer climates; it will therefore not stay where it falls but will (in the case of the Antarctic) be blown northward, perhaps hundreds of miles, out to sea. Likewise, temperature will affect the plasticity of many substances, including ice, so that a lowering of temperature may cause a diminution of glacial flow.

The actual snowfall in Antarctica is remarkably small. It is also unbelievably difficult to estimate, owing to the effects of wind, which, even in a dense blizzard, will often erode a surface, diminishing rather than raising a snow-level. This is frequently demonstrated by the characteristic way in which tracks of men, dogs and sledges are left in high relief where the looser surrounding snow has been blown away. Methods have been evolved to prove that millions of tons of snow are shifted annually over areas where the actual deposition is only a few inches. Of Adélie Land, it was estimated* that on each day of heavy blizzard 380,000 tons of snow passed out to sea over every mile of coastline. On the Ross Ice Shelf the total annual precipitation has been reckoned to be the equivalent of only about seven or eight inches of rain—a desert rainfall in Australia.

In cold climates snowfall is directly proportional to temperature; that is, less snow falls as it becomes colder. Antarctic air is also extremely dry, its absolute moisture content being low whatever its percentage of relative humidity (i.e. the water vapour it can sustain at any particular temperature).

* Dr F. Loewe, *Journal of Glaciology*, vol. 2, no. 19, March 1956, p. 664.

Wind is by far the most potent element in Antarctica. It converts loose snow into a howling, spiteful blizzard—the bewildering and dangerous white darkness that immobilizes, to a degree, all travellers and all means of transport. So drastically does it increase the effects of cold on human beings, by removing the superficial warm air trapped by the pores and hairs of the skin, by surface evaporation, and by disturbance of cushioned air held by clothing, that every knot of wind has been considered by some as being equal, in terms of human discomfort, to a fall of one degree in temperature. It is certain that —20°F. in calm conditions with the sun shining can be pleasant, but that much higher temperatures, even above zero, may be difficult to endure in a gale of wind, the chances of actual frostbite being infinitely higher.

Wind pressure rises very steeply with velocity. While a gale of 50 miles per hour will exert a pressure of under 8 pounds per square foot, a hurricane of 100 miles per hour will possess four times that power. Provided one has sufficient foot anchorage (on ice by means of strong crampons), it is possible to learn to struggle against such blasts, leaning at an angle which appears gravitationally absurd. The really high gusts may be extremely destructive, their pressures ranging upwards to more than 100 pounds to the square foot. This, of course, is why antarctic huts must be so strong and well guyed: the wall of a small building, 8 feet by 12 feet, might receive a sudden total pressure of something like four tons.

With wind usually rises drift, and with drift, humidity and frequently temperature. In the combination of these factors, through the temperature range of antarctic blizzards, lies danger and discomfort unless adequate shelter is available. It is certain that blizzard was a contributing factor, with deficiencies of diet and unsuitable transport, to the tragic end of Scott's expedition. If a party is immobilized—by the weather itself, or because it is impossible to navigate, or by dangerous crevassing in the area—then its food and fuel resources are taxed. In the case of Scott's party, very low temperatures (averaging —40°F. for weeks), inadequate food and hard man-hauling were the prime causes of disaster; their last hopes of reaching a depot, only a day's march away, were removed by blizzard.

Strong winds are more common in Antarctica, especially round the coast, than anywhere else on earth. The velocities of winds blowing down from the plateau may reach 80 to 100 miles an hour and may continue uniformly high for considerable periods; brief gusts may rise to 150 or more miles per hour. It seems that these hurricanes may occur anywhere round and near the coast of Antarctica but that at greater distances inland winds decrease in violence. Records from several I.G.Y. stations prove that some parts of the coast are more constantly windy than others, while far inland complete calms are far more common than anywhere near the sea. Sir Douglas Mawson's second winter season, in 1913, at his Cape Denison base (on the coast just east of Adélie Land) was one of the windiest ever recorded. On 5th July wind blew at an average speed of 107 miles per hour for eight hours on end. The average for the entire month was 63.3 miles per hour, and, for a year, about 50 miles per hour. Ever since Mawson's time the Adélie Land area has consistently been proved exceptionally windy by all parties wintering there. By contrast, at the Australian station named after Mawson an average velocity of only half that recorded at Cape Denison was registered during the windiest month of 1954 (June). It would appear that the average duration of severe weather at Mawson is shorter than at the Russian base at Mirny, only eight hundred miles to the east, and approximately twelve hundred miles west of the Adélie Land coast. From Mirny many reports of hurricanes exceeding 100 miles per hour were published during 1956-8.

In general terms, it is easy to account for the pattern of winds in Antarctica as part of a great air circulation in which north-bound low-level winds (deflected to the west by the rotation of the earth) stream out from Antarctica to compensate for large masses of warm tropical air moving south at great heights. All wind is caused primarily by a temperature differential, secondarily by the resulting pressure changes; it may also be modified by gravity, as are the winds that stream down the steep plateau perimeter in Antarctica. Although the theory of the movement of tropical air polewards and vice versa, as propounded in most elementary text-books, is without doubt basically correct, the more obvious modifications imposed by such factors as the rotation of the earth, the dome-like shape of Antarctica and its irregularities of surface and coastal configuration do not explain easily all the observed phenomena. For most of the century, up to the time of the International Geophysical Year, there were simply insufficient points of observation and insufficient data for analysis. Dr G. C. Simpson, the meteorologist with Scott's last expedition, proposed that a radial pressure wave system developed over Antarctica and accounted for disturbances over great distances, even beyond the Equator. By the time all the material of the I.G.Y. is evaluated an embracing analysis should be possible, especially as upper-air observations by radiosonde and radio-theodolite from many coastal and inland antarctic stations, and along selected meridians (10°E., 140°E. and within the longitudes 70°-80°W.) from Pole to Pole, will be available. Their collation into synoptic form may take a period of years, but already, from several sources, interim papers have appeared.

The high plateau of Antarctica is an immediate complication wherein the continent differs from all others. Only the sea coast, virtually, is at sea-level; everywhere else gravity must be a considerable component of weather. The winds from the interior receive a gravitational acceleration as they rush northward, and a strong westerly twist from the revolving world.

There is always a marked difference between the heating effects of the sea and of the ice at the coast or at the varying edge of the pack ice, where there is a tendency for the warmer air to rise over the cold. This is a so-called frontal region, which may move north or south according to season and the balance of contrary systems, and profoundly affect the weather of more temperate latitudes.

It is possible that the warmer sea air passes right over the cold air moving down from the plateau, into the central regions of the ice-cap. There must certainly be a distinct boundary between the two layers, maintained by their contrary movement, as well as by their differing densities. Not only the velocity but the deflection of winds becomes progressively greater as they move towards the coast; the former is aided by gravity and the latter by the increasing rotational speed of the earth's surface. The cores of the deflection movement and the temperature differential are not coincident: deflection (the east-west component) is centred by the geographical pole, tending to disappear there, while the temperature differential becomes progressively less until it disappears at the cold focus of the continent (the central highland farthest from the sea), where the upper air has descended and completed the cycle.

The winds leaving Antarctica are deflected more and more to the west. Ultimately they encounter a band of eastward-moving rising air of relatively low pressure. This constitutes an important polar front within which the deflected winds from the south may be contained for some days in a circumpolar stream above the well-known westerly coastal oceanic drift. It might be added here, since ocean movements have been mentioned, that there is a zone surrounding Antarctica in varying latitudes between approximately 45°S. and 60°S. where the cold surface water originating round the continent sinks below the warmer northern waters along a line of temperature differential known as the Antarctic Convergence.

It is a well-known physical principle that disturbances of a wave nature occur at the boundary between two moving fluids of differing densities. The common example, of course, is the waves caused by the wind over the surface of the sea. Once the movement commences it may reach considerable amplitude. Now, according to the proposed pattern of antarctic air movements, there are two distinct boundaries where wave motion may be engendered: firstly, that which separates the cold and warm air layers over the continent, and, secondly, that between the air surfaces at the polar front. At the former immense waves like ripples on a round pond will be propagated. These are of very long period, perhaps mainly seasonal, and of a wavelength about equal to the radius of the cold air bubble resting below the warm air mantle over the entire continent. Their main effect is to cause an oscillation—a seasonal shift—in the latitude of the polar front. It is possible that secondary waves are set up by mountain ranges and other anomalies causing regional variations.

The movement of the perimeter of the system will generate "scallop" waves in the polar front. These are usually of quite brief period (about twenty to twenty-four hours) but of wavelengths often exceeding a thousand miles. The whole polar system may now be pictured as a bubble of cold air overlain and enclosed by a warm layer. The height of the bubble—that is, to the point where the "inversion" between the layers of warm and cold air occurs—may range from about three thousand to seven thousand feet at the coast and becomes progressively less inland. At the coast, too, the differences in the velocity and temperature of the air streams are found to be most marked, the measurements being daily obtained by the use of radiosonde and other balloons carrying instruments that automatically transmit information to meteorologists on the ground and by tracking balloons by radiotheodolite.

It was discovered by Kochin that, in the northern hemisphere, similar "scallop" waves round the edge of the polar system became unstable and broke up into cyclonic disturbances if their wavelength exceeded about twelve hundred and fifty miles. The general conclusion may well be that this happens also in the south, mainly as a result of the confirmation and amplification of Dr Simpson's original theories by I.G.Y. observations. It explains the procession of short-duration cyclonic disturbances continually moving eastward in the "middle" latitudes of the southern oceans, the storm barrier that tosses all ships bound for Antarctica. And, when a great, slow, radial wave movement becomes unstable and breaks, then the whole cyclonic system may easily shift north to take in the inhabited continents—and cold antarctic air may cause southern Australia to shiver.

# 6

## MAMMALS OF THE SEA

By now, perhaps, this book has commenced to swing to the other extreme from that deplored early in Chapter 3. We have considered Antarctica as a huge bi-lobate mass, and learnt how man is showing the rock below to be more and more depressed as he fires his charges into the ice and calculates its thickness; we have taken a fairly wide look at the movements of ice and air; and we have used long-distance glasses to obtain a general sense of history. Now, perhaps, we may examine some aspects in detail and linger where there is most direct appeal. This part of the account should serve to show how very much of interest and importance concerning Antarctica must be left over after many volumes are written.

We have considered some of the gross aspects with which the human senses are capable of dealing. We have not considered the invisible forces of terrestrial magnetism, which have a moving focus in Antarctica; or one of the most beautiful and dramatic phenomena on earth, the aurora; or other perhaps less essentially polar occurrences which, nevertheless, are amongst the main objects of human interest in high latitudes.

It would be a lamentably incomplete account if the animals of the south passed unnoticed, both those from ancient time which pursued their finely balanced cycles thousands of years before man thought of Antarctica, and those which have come with him to pull his sledges.

Each age has its reasons for exploration; they and the ideals of the age change in composition even when they contain the same elements. The years bring new methods, new equipment. These are projections of images from something that exists in man; something that will change and develop and possibly wane. They are not part of the antarctic matrix; they are the implements which prise out its riches of both shadow and substance.

The Eskimos have a proverb, "Weather and Ice are kings". I first heard it quoted when a friend of mine was setting out over the sea ice with dogs on a long sledging journey along the coast of Antarctica.

"Weather and Ice are kings"! It is a brilliant folk-saying, combining truth and imagination with the utmost economy of words. But not many people ever experience such regal weather—which may blast and freeze and kill, over-riding plans and ventures, blotting out the world with furious grey blizzard, or which may be gracious and soft and clear . . . capricious like the old Norse gods. Few have seen the tremendous majesty of flashing icebergs or the endless white plain of the frozen sea that surrounds a land of perpetual glaciers. Here there is beauty, but it may only be accepted with the perils and chances—the moving berg driving on with inconceivable power; the shadowy, uncertain depths of crevasses; the clashing floes and the pressure of pack ice which can still make toys of man's stout ships. "Weather and Ice are kings"—in the Antarctic this has the same meaning as it had for the Eskimos of the northern polar twilight.

How does man live in this environment? The important thing of course is not to keep the cold out but to keep the heat in! No matter how thick or well insulated walls may be, they create no warmth. Without a stove the finest hut in the Antarctic would be as cold as a tomb; without the heat generated by the human body, eiderdowns and windproofs would be of no more value than feathers on a dead bird.

Heat—the warmth which allows life to continue—is always tending to escape. To understand the principles of holding heat it is important to remember that it escapes in three ways. The first is by being conducted away through a material, as heat from the end of the poker that is in a fire is transmitted to the handle. The second is by radiation through space, as the heat of the sun is transmitted to our skins even when the air is at a temperature below freezing. And the third is by convection (the movement upward of a fluid like air or water), as hot air and smoke go up the chimney, or hot water goes up to a storage tank in the rafters.

One of the very best insulators—that is, one of the poorest conductors of heat—is dry air. A carefully sealed wall-panel, with horizontal partitions to prevent all the warm air rising to the top, is a better insulator than an equal thickness of solid wood. Walls are therefore filled with air or, to prevent the development of convection currents and for added strength, with some porous material which holds air imprisoned in small pockets. There are several foamed plastics, rather like pumice in appearance, and mineral "wools" which act as suitable fillers.

Although the conduction of heat and its convection by air currents must be taken into account, radiation is almost always the most important cause of heat loss. Frequently, therefore, surfaces are silvered to reflect back the infra-red heat rays. Some of the most successful modern insulation has been achieved by building a wall of several sealed layers of air, horizontally partitioned against convection and separated vertically by thin sheets of brightly polished metal foil.

Ventilation, of course, is one of the great problems in huts in the Antarctic. The danger of foul air and carbon monoxide poisoning is equal to that of fire, probably the most consistent dread of all. Fresh air will flow in through a hole readily enough, but drift snow will be carried with it, and if this should be melted by the heat of the hut it may flow back, freeze, and seal the air inlet. The price of comfort and safety is watchfulness.

Clothing is designed on much the same principles as apply for buildings. Layers of air must be held close to the body. Foundation garments are singlets of thick but soft string mesh, knitted loosely to leave the maximum air spaces; and soft, loose underpants. The air that is warmed by the body remains held in position within the large pores of the mesh. Soft woollen clothes hold further air and provide ventilation. Outside everything is worn a windproof to prevent the cold air driving through and disturbing the cushions of warm air within. On the feet are worn lambswool inner boots over two or three pairs of thick soft socks, then insoles of spongy plastic mesh and outer boots of canvas, leather and rubber containing no nails to conduct away the warmth of the feet.

At times considerable perspiration must occur even in Antarctica. As the warmed and humid air gradually escapes outwards from the body, it reaches a layer where frost is formed. It's a little odd at night in a tent to strip off your windproofs and outer woollens and find a layer white and glistening with hoar. Below your insoles, too, as often as not, your boots are full of it. A newer type of footwear provides double rubber walls impermeable to perspiration and separated by air held in soft foamed plastic, synthetic wool or some other suitable medium. On this "vapour barrier" principle have been evolved the lightest highly insulated boots for really low temperatures. They possess the disadvantage of all hermetically sealed garments, the trapping of moisture on the skin itself. Still, by most men damp warmth is preferred to dry cold, and it is less dangerous. The minimum of socks required are quickly changed and dried as opportunities permit. Men travelling in aircraft and other vehicles, or standing for long periods of observation in intense cold, are enthusiastic about the unventilated boot. It is just as well no one in Antarctica worries about fashions.

I have mentioned drift snow many times. Antarctic drift is as fine and dry as talcum powder, clouding the air so evenly that its streaming movement is invisible even when gusts suddenly increase its density. There is no appearance of flying flakes—just an ebb and flow of shadow. Drift snow is the most extraordinarily penetrating substance, finding a

way through the smallest crack in a hut or a vehicle. I have
heard men softly cursing as they pursued some minute hole
that was letting in buckets of drift, speaking much as men
might while hunting lice in the desert, and suddenly ejacu-
late in triumph as though they had conquered a little living
beast.

Of course, man is an interloper and as such he deserves
some inconvenience. Nature decreed millions of years ago
that all living things depart from the Antarctic—depart or
perish, or else adapt themselves to the least hospitable environment on earth. Vegetable life mostly perished or re-
tained a lowly lichened grip on coastal rocks, suspending all
growth except for a few weeks in summer. Many lowly
forms of animal life adapted themselves or evolved a
specialized existence below the ice in sub-freezing salt water;
a few higher animals, so the evidence seems to say, changed
their forms and habits to a remarkable degree, through a
million generations, to enable them to cope with conditions
and prey on the multitudinous oceanic hordes.

Evolution is one of the most disturbing and convenient
concepts in man's philosophy. It is convenient to say that
penguins gave up flight through air in some Tertiary paradise
before any faint approach to human thought existed; that
they evolved flippers and streamlined bodies to fly through
water at incredible speed and evade cruel leopard seals, whose
own dim ancestors with legs, earthbound in early Eden,
would have constituted a lesser foe for birds. But, however
perfect the theory, the necessary natural selection, equated
even with infinite time and chance and mutation, is difficult
and disturbing to conceive.

With a solitary exception all the higher animals became
seasonal visitors, retreating to the open sea, the edge of the
ice or more temperate lands for the long months of winter,
and returning only for the brief silver summer. The exception was the Weddell seal, who lives through the winter in
the warmer waters below the sea ice—their warmth being

entirely relative, (for they are colder than the freezing point
of fresh water). But he had to pay a tremendous price for
his daring. Being a mammal he must breathe air, so, throughout the many months when the sea is frozen and the air too
cold for him to emerge with impunity, he must keep a
breathing hole open in the thick sea ice, or suffocate by
drowning. This he does by constantly biting and rasping the
edges of his hatchway to the bitter world. And when he
grows too old or his teeth are worn too low, he dies.

There are several other seals in antarctic waters, some
preferring the sub-antarctic islands or the pack ice for breeding, but all, at least seasonally, visiting the continent. The
ponderous elephant seal is especially common at islands such
as Heard, Macquarie and South Georgia; it appears to be
completely at home in its muddy wallows on the Iles de
Kerguelen. The bull of this species may attain a weight of
several tons and a length of seventeen feet. He is a harem
lord, preferring the beaches of the cold desert islands, where
he may attract a hundred wives; their pups at birth may
weigh eighty pounds, and by the time they are weaned of
mother's milk they may reach nearly four hundredweight.

On the same beaches, especially at Heard Island, may be
observed the silver-grey and spotted leopard seals, or sea-
leopards, sleek carnivorous monsters whose diet is very
largely composed of the gentoo and rockhopper penguins
of sub-antarctic latitudes. They range these seas for food
and lie up in considerable numbers on the black volcanic
sands of Heard, perhaps to rest from the eternally turbulent
sea, but they have their young amongst the ice-floes farther
south.

The seals (Pinnipedia) may be divided into two great
families—the true or earless seals (Phocidae) and the eared
seals (Otariidae). The former do not use their limbs in any
way as legs, progressing on shore or on ice by convulsive
wave-like movements of the body; the latter may use their
flippers as legs, virtually walking upon them, and on shore

*ANARE photo: W. R. J. Dingle*

Adélies in one of their ancestral mating areas. They assemble while the sea is still frozen.

Light-mantled sooty albatrosses at a nesting site on Heard Island. The white mark near the eye is a plumage feature, not part of the eye.

*ANARE photo: John Béchervaise*

*ANARE photo: Phillip Law*
Silver-grey petrel and chick on a rock-ledge on an island off the Wilkes Coast.

Birds of a feather! A giant petrel alights among a flock of cape pigeons (also members of the petrel family) near Davis.
*ANARE photo: W. R. J. Dingle*

the hind limbs are turned forwards like feet. The Phocidae are represented in the Antarctic by the Weddell, crabeater, leopard, Ross, and elephant seals. The last-named has always been considered more a sub-antarctic than a truly antarctic species, but its prevalence along the rocky coasts of the Vestfold Hills area of the mainland, noted by Australian observers at Davis (founded 1957), makes it appear that ice rather than a high latitude is disliked by the big elephants. However, the elephant seal differs from the other antarctic Phocidae in seldom being solitary or favouring small groups. All seals are polygamous but in this respect the elephant outclasses them all.

The southern fur seal is quite rare nowadays, never having recovered from the ruthless depredations of the nineteenth century. It is the only eared seal that was of commercial importance in southern waters. Fanning (1832) claimed that more than a hundred thousand fur seals were slaughtered in a single year (1800) in South Georgia alone, and Biscoe estimated that about a million and a quarter skins had been taken from the same island in the half-century ending in 1825 (that is, since Cook's voyages). Possibly every colony was virtually exterminated. In the latter part of the nineteenth century it seemed that the species might become extinct; it may now possess, in all, a few thousand individuals. The fur seal is not a large animal, adults seldom exceeding six feet in length. The fur of the adults varies somewhat in colour but may be a very warm brown or a rich fawn. A few specimens are now seen regularly on most of the sub-antarctic islands.

The southern sea-lion, the South Australian sea-lion, Hooker's sea-lion, and probably other related species are also eared, but their pelts are coarse and were never valuable. Their yield of oil never approached that of the elephant seal.

One of the rarer true or earless seals of the Antarctic is that named after Ross. It is short and fat with a striated throat which it expands quite grotesquely. Several times I

F

have encountered the species: once on Heard Island, where a juvenile came ashore and lingered for a day, allowing himself to be photographed from all angles, once on a large ice-floe in Prydz Bay (antarctic mainland, 75°E.) and occasionally at sea in pack ice.

The crabeater seal is the most abundant of all, but it is mainly to be found in the rather uncomfortable vicinity of the pack-ice edge. It has been exploited for its skin and blubber, about fifty thousand adult animals being taken from the northern Weddell Sea in the 1892-3 season. The later sealers always had a major interest in blubber and oil and, ultimately, the industry based on these largely supplanted that based on fur. On Heard Island, at the time of the *Challenger* expedition (1874-5), there were still forty sealers scattered in parties along the coast, rendering down the blubber of elephant seals, but by then the greater days of all sealing were over. I often used to come upon the remains of great iron try-pots, relics of the oil-renderers, rusted and half-buried in the sands and cushion-plants of Heard Island beaches and headlands.

All seals, at some time or another, haul themselves out of the sea and rest or breed on land or ice. The whales (Cetacea) are completely marine and therefore, perhaps, do not enter into accounts of Antarctica as much as do the seals and penguins. But, on the other hand, they have been the greatest magnet of all towards the antarctic regions and, to date, their exploitation has brought great material return to man. Whales and seals have been hunted for at least a thousand years for their flesh and their oil, the latter having been used for lighting, heating and lubrication, and for the treatment of wool and leathers since very early times. Today, whale oil is commonly employed as an additive to mineral oils, but in many of its older uses it has been supplanted by oils refined from those of the wells, by other fuels or by electricity. However, the chemical hydrogenation of whale oil enables it to be used for both margarine and soap, and innumerable other derivatives. Every part of the whale is now utilized, much of it, directly or indirectly, for human consumption as food or medicine; even the percentage of flesh and bone converted to fertilizers has meant an increase in the food yield of the world.

From the apical viewpoint of the mammal man, the mammal whale is amongst the most efficient food-producers. Whales do naturally precisely what man may eventually be forced to attempt synthetically; that is, they produce food from its elements. In fact, they make use of intermediate stages—plant and animal plankton, which successively convert the nutrient chemical resources of the sea into the bulk of living bodies. Some whales—the baleen species (of the order Mysticeti)—take the minute plankton directly as food; others—of the toothed species (Odontoceti), which include relatively small members such as dolphins and porpoises—feed upon fish and squid and higher forms of life, as do the seals and seabirds.

Round the antarctic coasts, for an average distance of perhaps a thousand miles, anyway as far as the Antarctic Convergence (see p. 56), there is a closed cycle of planktonic life depending on many factors, including the arrival from the north of rich deep currents which deposit vast quantities of organic matter, the marked seasonal changes, and a lower salinity (than that of lower latitudes). It is a complicated cycle and a fuller discussion is not warranted here, but, in effect, it ensures that antarctic seas are rich in the salts required for incalculable numbers of minute plant plankton which, in turn, provide assimilable food for animal life. The existence of the primary forms of the latter—the zooplankton, the smallest kinds of shrimp-like and other animals—provides the answer to the old wonderment, "Master, I marvel how the fishes live in the sea." It is an answer which differs little from that of the sage, "Why, as men do a-land ... the great ones eat up the little ones"! This is more than a mere proverb; it is a succinct statement concerning the cycle of life (but, remember, it is still metaphorical in that no cetacean is a fish!).

*Plankton,* by derivation and definition, connotes those forms of life which are moved by the ocean's currents, which drift within its surface or submarine cycles. It includes not only the microscopic organisms but larger creatures with a limited power of adaptation to variations in salinity and temperature. If, in fact, the organisms drift beyond their climatic zones they die and eventually sink to the bottom and revert to their constituent substances.

The high concentration of plankton or secondary forms of life in antarctic waters attracts whales and seals. Because of the intense cold they have converted some of the planktonic substance for protection and developed enormous thicknesses of fatty blubber beneath the skin. This blubber is also a surplus food store, especially for use during breeding excursions to warmer zones. For man, it yields the valuable oil— averaging something over ten tons to the beast. All species move towards convenient summer latitudes or conditions to bear their young. The precise life-histories of all economic species have now been under study for a long period; the basic life of the minutiae of the southern oceans has been investigated much more recently. In sum, all the facts are becoming sufficiently well known to enable the whaling industry to be pursued intelligently, with a view to conservation of all species. I do not think there can be any doubt that the world of the future for a long time to come will increasingly need the assistance of the plankton-whale cycle and other such. Wise legislation will eventually recognize the human species, materially, as part of the general balance, and all organic remains will be justly returned to suitable entry points of the circles of life.

The whales hunted today are, of the toothed group, mainly the sperm whale, which dives deeply, feeds mainly on squid, and roves the world; and, of the baleen group, the humpback, fin, sei, and blue whales, the last being the largest, reaching possibly a hundred feet in length. It should be explained that the baleen species possess, instead of teeth, sieve-curtains of the flexible material (baleen) which was the old "whalebone" of commerce, of greatest value before the age of synthetic plastics.

The dolphins of the toothed species include the ferocious killer whale, twenty to thirty feet long, a truly carnivorous monster which attacks, in schools, most of his cetacean relations as well as the seals. The killers have apparently consolidated as an instinct the habit of over-toppling ice-floes on which seals are at rest and would doubtless be indiscriminative of diet if they upset an odd hunter or antarctic explorer. Another of the beasts' unpleasant habits is to break a floe from beneath to investigate a promising shadow. Shackleton and his team were not a little displeased with the possibility of this happening while they were drifting on the ice of the Weddell Sea in 1915.

The other evident "killer" of the Antarctic, the much smaller leopard seal, may restrict his diet mainly to penguins. He certainly does not attack anything when he is out of the water. Many times I have watched penguins strolling unconcernedly within easy reach of the evil-looking tight mouths of leopards, and I myself have walked amongst them without their evincing the slightest appetitive interest. In water this seal is in an entirely different element; there he is swift, sudden and ruthless death to penguins. He patrols just outside the breakers, often as not, of a beach where the penguins land—and the wash of the sea is filled with the skins of the birds.

The famous right whale, one of the greatest species of commerce, was relentlessly hunted for centuries, gradually being harried to its most distant retreats. It was easier to catch than most whales, being a slower swimmer. Both its baleen and its oil were plentiful and of good quality. The same sort of exploitation as the fur seals suffered eventually brought the creature to near extinction, and, by a reasonable

measure of international agreement, it is now totally protected. However, the gradual improvements in technique
made it possible to capture the faster, deeper-diving whales.
Weapons of great power and accuracy have been invented to
replace the old harpoon, and not only have the chasing
vessels grown from small and treacherous shore-based craft,
rowed by man, to fast diesel vessels of 400-500 tons with
great power (up to 2000 horse-power) for their size, but
the flensing stations, where the whales are cut up and the
blubber is rendered down, have themselves taken to the
open ocean as factory ships with stern ramps and tackle capable of lifting whales whole out of the water. It is to these
factory ships that the fleets of chasers are now attached. By
the middle of the present century there were between twenty
and thirty of these great floating factories in operation round
Antarctica, and each mother craft had up to ten chasers.
The season's work for each factory ship might be worth
anything up to £1,500,000. As many as forty thousand
whales have been captured in antarctic waters in a single year
of this century, but today the numbers of all baleen whales
to be taken are limited and, even augmented by the unre-
stricted sperm whales, the total whale catch is not likely to
be so high. Of fifty-five thousand whales of all species killed
throughout the world in the year 1954-5 thirty-eight thous-
and were taken in antarctic waters. These whales yielded two
and a quarter million barrels of oil, eighty-one per cent of
the whale oil of the world. It is of interest, in passing, to
mention that about two thousand whales are annually taken
in Australian waters, the total oil production being approximately one hundred thousand barrels (each one-sixth of a
ton).

It says something for man's collective common sense that
in whaling, as in geophysics, there has been great international co-operation in the Antarctic. The basis for it all has
been the scientific work in oceanography and marine biology

carried out by many expeditions since the famous cruise of the *Challenger*.

Apart from the information gained from the purely exploratory and scientific voyages, knowledge of the various species has been added to by all the whalers. Much material, both qualitative and statistical, has been published in this century, especially by Norwegians, who, from its first decade have taken a leading part in the development of antarctic whaling. Britain has maintained vessels for oceanographical research since 1920, when Scott's *Discovery* was purchased. It became the Royal Research Ship *Discovery* and has since been succeeded by R. R. S. *William Scoresby* and R. R. S. *Discovery II*, both still active in research and exploratory work.

Major projects in oceanography and marine biology were undertaken by several of the nations which set up antarctic stations during the International Geophysical Year.

# 7

# LIFE ABOVE THE ICE

WE have considered how man lives in Antarctica; how he conserves warmth. This is, in fact, fairly easy in an established base or even aboard a ship. It is possible to warm and insulate huts and cabins so that their occupants can feel literally at home in controlled conditions of temperature and humidity requiring no special clothing or other protection. Very often the difference of temperature between external and internal conditions will exceed 100°F. Generally huts are provided with uninsulated porches in which men may gain shelter from wind and drift, remove outer garments and hang them where snow in their folds will remain unthawed. Straw whisks or brushes are always provided for the removal of the dust-like snow, but if men are going in and out of huts during a blizzard they will often leave clothes unbrushed in the porch until they require them again. Except for cost and inconvenience, there are no bars to men and women living comfortably in the world's most rigorous climate; both impediments could yield to sufficiently strong economic and human reasons. I think, in the fullness of time, they will do so.

Away from base there may be calm sunny weather when the radiant heat of the sun is pleasantly warm, but a man must never be far from the clothing he will certainly require at short notice. He may be travelling on foot, with dogs, in motor vehicles such as weasels or sno-cats, or by aeroplane. While engines are running it is usually possible to channel some of their warmth back into the cabin, but during the halts it is hard to maintain adequate insulation from the outside elements. While a meal is being prepared even the heat from a kerosene pressure stove is welcome. Ventilation is also a problem in the restricted space of a weasel cabin, particularly if the air is filled with flying drift.

Well garbed, a man may be sufficiently comfortable in temperatures as low as —30°F. or —40°F., provided he is protected from the wind. A tent, well pitched and anchored with sufficient snow or *névé* blocks, is at least as comfortable to sleep in as a modern vehicle. Sleeping bags are insulated from the hard and cold surface of the ice by mattresses of sponge rubber or quilted blocks of foamed plastic. Men gradually become adept at performing all sorts of tasks in heavy gloves, removing the outer mitts only when a quality of special precision is essential.

Of course, pitching and striking tents takes time, especially in wind and drift. There are occasions when a motor vehicle, towing sledge caravans, can take advantage of brief lulls in the weather and proceed over valuable miles when there would be insufficient time, and possibly resolution, to break camp. In modern exploration mechanized travel is inevitable. Men and supplies put down by plane may enable a maximum number of precious summer days to be spent in far inland areas. There are still complex problems of lubricants and engine operation on the high, cold plateau. A plane requires super-chargers, at least to rise with a full load at high altitudes. However, the solution of all difficulties is well within the capacity of modern technology. The problems of the terrain itself are less simply solved.

American engineers, during the International Geophysical Year, constructed a safe "road", more than six hundred miles long, from Little America to their inland station Byrd (lat. 80°S., long. 120°W.) by blasting, bulldozing and filling in crevasses. On the plateau, ice may be regarded as a white rock to be hewn or crushed and used in building or road-making. However, it is not feasible to build roads while exploring new territory and, unfortunately, amongst the mountains crevasses are often so common as to make the use of tractors and other vehicles impossible. In the Prince Charles Mountains, two hundred miles south of Mawson, my weasels came upon dangerous crevassing some miles from the nearest exposed rock, and in the following season (1956-7) Bewsher and Crohn considered travel amongst the peaks impossible without dogs.

Sledge dogs have long been bred in the arctic countries of the far north, and those in Antarctica, or their ancestors, were recruited from Labrador, Alaska and Greenland. The dogs used by recent Australian (ANARE) expeditions, also three teams taken by Hillary to the Ross Dependency (New Zealand territory), were bred on Heard Island and at Mawson from stock left in Melbourne by a French expedition in 1949.

They are big dogs, huskies, weighing up to a hundred pounds or more, and varying considerably in build and appearance, some being much rougher-coated than others. Their dense pelt gives them adequate protection from cold, and they live tranquilly in the open, provided temperatures do not rise high enough for them to become wet. They curl up in dry snow and allow themselves to be almost buried by drift. Quarrelsome amongst themselves, they are usually quite gentle towards their human masters. Their harness is constructed from tough flexible webbing, and various kinds of traces are used to suit the terrain. Dogs in tandem—one after another on a long centre-trace—possess great pulling power, but fan-traces—each dog on a separate lead—are safer in crevassed ice.

Loads have frequently averaged one hundred pounds weight per dog on sea ice and good plateau surfaces. Stefansson reported dog teams pulling an average of two hundred pounds per dog for a thousand miles in the Arctic. Dogs, flown inland to mountain areas, are proving their superlative value even in these days of mechanization. Anyone who has travelled with dogs has mixed memories, but he recalls the companionship of his teams with affection and their gallant service with gratitude.

In this kind of travelling, men are, of course, fully exposed to the weather, and for warmth they will frequently ski or run alongside or ahead of the dogs, even when loads are sufficiently light for them to ride the sledges. A man should be very fit physically when sledging; he should be able, if necessary, to travel on foot as long and as far as his dogs.

Evening and morning are the busy times. In the evening those in charge of the dogs proceed with feeding, unharnessing and tethering while other men erect tents and prepare the meal. Usually at night the dogs are tired. In the mornings, during the harnessing, they are lively and quarrelsome. A disagreement may develop with extraordinary suddenness and convert a well-ordered team into a howling, fighting mob, with traces tangled almost inextricably and with all dogs seemingly athirst for blood. To such difficulties may be added the whine and bewilderment of blizzard, when the world is lost and you are blindfolded by swirling, cubic whiteness.

Man shares the antarctic winter with only one other living creature besides the dog—the emperor penguin. I shall always associate dog and penguin, for it was at the end of a long August journey with dogs, over the sea ice, that I first visited a rookery of the immense birds. For a day or two before reaching the main congregation (at the Taylor Glacier, about seventy miles along the coast west of Mawson) we encountered solitary birds. I recall my first sight of a group of emperors promenading by a pressure crack in the ice. Nine huge birds provided a strange display, unlike any other manifestation of bird behaviour. They strutted and bowed and stood in statuesque groups ignoring our presence. We were on the fringe of emperor penguin territory, the domain of tall, proud birds which survive more fearful conditions than any other creatures on earth.

Even in the dull light of the overcast and snowing sky, their pale, creamy-yellow breasts shone like satin, and the vivid chrome patches on both sides of their heads were brighter than anything else in Antarctica except the sunset sky. The big birds had black, expressionless eyes and carbon black heads which absorbed all light, so that they seemed almost two-dimensional, except for the curved streaks of their purple-pink bills. They waddled along in a comical yet tremendously dignified fashion, lifting their heads from time to time to utter an extraordinarily penetrating, resonant cry like the sound of a concertina abruptly starting and, after half a second, as suddenly ending.

Just before a blizzard descended upon us we noticed individuals or small groups of penguins processing over the ice. We just managed to reach a small island. As dusk fell the weather cleared a little. Immense icebergs were grounded all around us; some revealed enormous pressure cracks from base to summit. The failing light robbed them of substance but not of size. There was a leaden stillness, with the forlorn cries of the loneliest birds in the world sounding eerily through the long sub-zero night.

With the size of the emperor penguin—he may weigh up to ninety pounds and stand erect at three feet six—is bound up his whole problem of rearing a family of one solitary chick. The seasonal break-out of sea ice occurs, as a rule, in January or February. The midsummer period of continuous daylight is then over, but at least the open water is at its nearest to the continent. This, therefore, is obviously the time for adolescent penguins, in fact for all young birds, to make their first acquaintance with the sea. The smaller species, such as the Adélie—the common penguin of the antarctic coasts—are able to assemble, mate and produce well-fledged youngsters within the relatively fine months of summer—from October to February. They grow at a prodigious rate, nurtured on food regurgitated by their parents. Fortunately, their increasing demands for food are generally matched by its greater availability as the ice break-up gains impetus.

The emperor chick also makes his first acquaintance with the sea in January and February. But, unlike his smaller cousins, he cannot reach near maturity in the few brief summer months; he is just too big. Neither could he grow fast enough from a one-pound egg, nor could his parents stuff him with sufficient food. So it is that the most extraordinary breeding cycle has been evolved by the emperors.

The adults converge on their rookery sites in March or early April, swimming, or trekking over the newly frozen sea, according to season. They make good speed by lying prone on the ice and tobogganing on their breasts, propelling themselves with feet and flippers. All known rookeries are either on floating ice or on rock-based ice connected to the sea. In a period of more than fifty years less than twenty breeding colonies have been located around the entire coast of the antarctic continent. The Taylor Glacier rookery was discovered by Dovers and Schwartz in 1954, while they were engaged in coastal survey.

When the birds are assembled, there commences a period of elaborate ceremonial. The penguins promenade, bow to each other, display their magnificence and converse with cries very different from the lonely concertina calls of the sea ice. Male and female use different forms of a similar cry. According to members of the notable 1952 French expedition in Adélie Land (who spent a year in observing the emperors), this is the only aspect of the birds' behaviour which instantly defines the sexes. The culmination of the courtship and mating is the laying of a solitary egg per couple in the month of May, about two months after the birds first muster. Consider the position! Neither bird has eaten for two months, the sea is frozen far beyond the horizon, the great penguins are brooding nestless on naked ice, and the darkness, the blizzards and extreme cold of winter are upon the coasts of Antarctica.

It is then that the females, who have treasured their eggs on their black horny feet for no more than twenty-four hours, shielding them beneath their pendulous bodies, suddenly decamp, leaving their precious eggs to the fathers. They allow them to roll gently onto the ice, then, with stately and graceful movements, they depart for distant horizons and the remote square meal they must at all costs discover. The male birds eagerly claim the eggs, placing them upon their feet and covering them with their lower breasts.

For two months father patiently incubates the egg. When blizzards are so bitter that life itself is threatened, the big birds slowly shuffle together until they rest in one great huddle, exposing a minimum of body area to the blast. The females return in excellent condition, ready to take over the hatched chicks, to feed them with regurgitated shrimp-paste and other planktonic or fishy delicacies. Again the penguins cry, each to each, until they recognize their mates. The male bird, emaciated and dull after four months as lover, husband and father, waddles slowly away to the north. But he will return.

There is, as may be imagined, considerable infant mortality all along the line. Eggs are frozen or broken, often by an excess of solicitude; small youngsters are trampled on as the birds huddle together during a storm; parents fall to fierce predators such as leopard seals out in the northern waters and their chicks eventually starve and perish.

Late in the afternoon of the day we left the island, we sighted the actual rookery. Alongside the blue tongue of glacial ice that projected far out through the sea ice, there appeared a smudge out of tone and keeping with all the rest of the world of ice. From miles away we saw it as we raced over the frosty sea. And then, slowly, the smudge gained texture until it became an assembly of great standing birds, nearly all bearing on their horny feet grey chicks which peered forth with white-ringed eyes.

One of the strangest effects of all was auditory. Each

chick piped with the voice of a singing bird, such as one might hear in a summer garden, only very much louder and richer. It was the sweetest natural sound I ever heard in Antarctica.

There were still many months to go before the chicks would be ready to leave the rookery. A month later a party from Mawson found them able to move away from their parents and to form small protective huddles of their own. Their rapid growth towards summer freedom and self-sufficiency required foraging by both parents now. Over the white sea ice there must be endless comings and goings, effort almost beyond imagination, so that a new generation might be launched in its right season.

The little Adélie penguins are known everywhere round the coasts and off-shore islands of Antarctica. Their behaviour often resembles that of the emperors, but they mate at the beginning of a summer and, as a rule, are able to rear their one or two offspring before the sea refreezes.

So often in discussing any grand theme in limited time or space, one faces the alternatives of being summary, scientific and comprehensive or of taking but a small part and endeavouring to illumine it sufficiently to cause one's listeners or readers to want to discover ways of exploring the rest for themselves. I have used both these methods in this little book. There is the third way: that of touching swiftly and lightly on many facets almost at random; this method ought to indicate that the field is vast and fascinating, and certainly worth further examination by those whose interest is stimulated. I should like to make this sort of approach in completing my chapter on antarctic birds. In an appendix I shall list scientific names.

The staunch little Adélie penguin, known to all antarctic voyagers, is the true harbinger of the far southern summer. You may encounter him quite alone in the late spring making his way steadily over the frozen sea, the forerunner of millions that have felt the urgent call to propagate their kind and that are following somewhere behind him over the white northern horizon. At about the same time the swift, keen-eyed skuas—the preying birds of the Antarctic—arrive by air, also in ones and twos. Both return to the harsh nesting islands and headlands of their ancestors, where, as the summer matures, there will be many hours of sun-warmed rock.

The ceremonies of the Adélies' courtship, however instinctive and automatic they may be in the opinion of modern biological scientists, are strangely moving to the observer. Comical perhaps they are, as the rather plain little penguins promenade and raise their bumpy heads in desperate cries of hope or annunciation; human emotions are stirred pleasantly by all the apparent ceremony of the courtship and mating. But there is pathos in the way the penguins solemnly collect the loose stones used by countless generations of birds and present them to each other to make the crude stone circles which serve as nests. The stones are scattered by a year's blizzards, are frozen hard to the rocks by the salt spray, but they will be aired and sunned and rearranged in the future, times without number.

The Adélie, as a species, suffers from two frightful dangers: that the pack ice will not break out sufficiently for food-gathering by the parents, and that the sea will refreeze before the young are ready to leave the colonies. There is ample evidence that these events occur from time to time, for the hollows and recesses of many coastal and island rookeries are dense with the bodies of almost mature chicks, dehydrated but not decomposed. It is difficult to distinguish the generations of the dead; perhaps they are separated by five or ten years, but time alters them very little. Parent birds have been observed travelling very great distances in efforts to bring food to their young, but, once in a while, "weather and ice" are fatally tyrannous.

With many variations, penguin life continues through every southern latitude almost to the Equator. Australians, South Africans and South Americans are all familiar with

*ANARE photo: John Béchervaise*

Launching a meteorological balloon at Mawson. The valuable and fragile radiosonde and rawin ("radio wind") transmitters will be released when the cord linking them to the balloon is sufficiently extended.

*ANARE photo: K. B. Mather*

Exploding a charge during seismic ice-sounding operations on the antarctic plateau. The drilling machine is on the sledge just to the right of the discharge column.

their home species whose hardier cousins remained in the south. The greatest band of all seabird life lies in the middle latitudes of the 'forties and 'fifties, where islands provide nesting places—for what other reason would any bird of the sea come to dull land?—and seasons to suit the various species. I cannot describe all the sub-antarctic penguins, even of the Australian territories. There are the vociferous, indignant macaronis, and their close Macquarie Island relations, the royals. Both have fine golden crests and make a splendid sight along the black rocks of a spray-swept littoral. They appear rather uppish towards the eternally surprised little rockhoppers, with their side-feathered heads decorated as though by wisps of pale yellow straw. The gentoos are quieter and more sedate; they are uncrested, but attractively flecked in maturity on the head and neck. The ring or "chin-strap" penguin looks like his nickname, his black cap quite evidently held in position. All these more northern relatives of the Adélie resemble him in some respects; perhaps all penguins possess more obvious resemblances than differences. They all balance their lives very critically with the seasons.

The king is the brightest, sleekest and most mobile of all penguins. He is becoming fairly well known in appearance, since he manages, from time to time, to survive the indignity of removal to zoological concentration camps. If ever you should see him in his glory on such places as the green, windy coastlands of Kerguelen, or the shingle beaches of Macquarie Island, you will gaze fascinated by his golden ear-patches, his blue-black cloak, and his saffron, satin breast, by his graceful movements in a serried company—and you will know that he must be only half alive away from the windy sub-antarctic. Every penguin I have mentioned, even the Adélie and the emperor (in the latter case a juvenile well off course), came ashore at Heard Island while I was there with an ANARE party in 1953-4.

In the summer the far south is visited by skuas, representing the gull family (Lariformes), and by several of the

G

petrels (Procellariidae). Watchful for unguarded eggs or chicks, the McCormick skua is a fearsome predator, always wheeling round the Adélie rookeries and the burrows or nesting crannies of the petrels. No guileless or unwary bird is safe in the Antarctic; somewhere the beady eyes of the skua are watching. The little black and white storm petrels fly erratically and the snow petrels rise and fall and flutter like blown papers to avoid the arrow-swift flight of the skua. Life is so finely balanced along the antarctic coasts, harsh even in summer. Many times I have watched the birds constantly wheeling over the granite arms and drifting floes of Mawson harbour, often in the bright summer midnight, with all the bergs flushed golden far out on the northern horizon.

The skua feasts from living prey or carrion and yet appears in a manner fastidious, retaining his dignity even amongst the offal of a seal killed for the dogs. The birds are generally to be seen in pairs and they share any food either may capture. They frequently nest close to a colony of Adélie penguins, swiftly stealing whatever is left unguarded. The McCormick skua is not infrequently met far inland, high up on the antarctic plateau; his cousin, the southern skua, is very common in the sub-antarctic. Both find warmer winter quarters, but, generally speaking, the northern limit of the antarctic species does not coincide with the southern limit of his cousin.

Of the flying birds actually nesting on the continent, one might make particular mention of a series already briefly referred to above. This is the exquisite snow petrel, pure white except for black bill and feet, which breeds not only in coastal rock-clefts but in crannies of mountains far inland. It arrives in flocks, often flying so high in the bitter air that the birds are lost to sight. Most of the petrels find food among the pack ice and brash, where, as a result of waves upsetting floes, great numbers of small shrimps and other crustaceans are often isolated and exposed. There is frequently, also, organic matter left undigested or rejected by the larger marine mammals.

The islands of the sub-antarctic latitudes possess a far greater wealth of bird life than the continent. Albatrosses, petrels, terns, gulls and cormorants breed on them, choosing their favourite terrains either inside or outside the Antarctic Convergence. The bird life of Kerguelen, for instance, differs quite markedly from that of Heard Island, only three hundred miles away but within the Convergence and, as a result, bearing proportionately a much greater area of permanent ice.

The great wandering albatross, which, like the emperor penguin, has a chick to nourish beyond a summer's kindly span, prefers the warmer islands. It is a never-to-be-forgotten experience to come upon a huge solitary bird brooding amongst the spare herbage. Like all birds of the far south she displays little fear, but she may rise quite composedly and spread her tremendous wings eight or ten feet, a little in the manner adopted in her earlier courtship display dance, while you stand utterly fascinated and astounded. It is so very different an experience from that of watching the peerless wanderer wave-skimming at sea, where she is really in her perfect element. A wandering albatross on land seems to have strayed from a Sinbad fable.

The lesser albatrosses breed amongst the cliff crags, most species on ancestral nests which may be pedestalled by many years' accretion of mud, vegetation and guano. Few ornithological delights can equal that of spending two or three hours on the ledges of a high cliff-face, watching the black-brows or the light-mantled sooties sweep in from the sea and fearlessly alight beside you.

# 8

## SOUTHERN LIGHTS

THERE are many reasons why men have always been attracted by Antarctica. Some find the old atavistic call of adventure strong enough and sufficient; all hear it and know its influence. Many have been lured by the rich organic wealth of the far south seas. A few, doubtless, have sought the renown of being first-footers in a new area or a new era. Some have been inspired by chances of discovering reefs and minerals; others only desire to add to the wealth of man's knowledge. With most antarctic voyagers some or all of these reasons are blended in varying degrees; no one's motives remain unchanged as the years pass. The most prosaic fortune-seeker, of knowledge, fur, oil or minerals, becomes illumined by the flare of romance. He has stood wide-eyed beneath the aurora, and he will recall it and all its associations to the end of his days.

In the Antarctic, still to be tapped, there is a great reservoir of matter of scientific interest of a kind that not only appeals to man's inquiring spirit but nourishes the very qualities that make him human. That eventually it may be linked with his material wealth and comfort may be of incidental concern to the scientist as such, but, generally, the same man is sufficiently humble and just to hope that what he finds will eventually prove of double wealth to mind and body. It is this quick sympathy with the more practical aims of an expedition that makes a good scientist a good explorer —and a good companion. He understands how fully he must lean on the essential services of the far south, and his close friends are the men who provide power, maintain health, cook meals, service vehicles and build huts. On Australian

(ANARE) expeditions all the routine chores at base are evenly rostered within the whole party, each man taking a day's duty every fortnight or three weeks.

Meteorology has always ranked high amongst antarctic sciences. In these days of national expeditions, when the antarctic explorer is a civil servant, the whole meteorological programme is part of the national plan to understand and forecast the weather for the sake of the country's primary producers and for the general convenience of its people. It must fit, however, within the wider geophysical frame of the world, whose weather is indivisible and, like peace or science, cannot be arbitrarily partitioned. For many years Australian expeditions have been under the aegis of the External Affairs Department of the Commonwealth Government, which, however, has wisely delegated virtually all control, other than financial, to its Antarctic Division and the Antarctic Planning Committee. These co-ordinate the contributions of the Departments of the Navy, the Army, and Air—all doing much on the logistical side—and the Departments of the Interior (meteorology), National Development (geophysics, geology and mapping) and Primary Industry (fisheries, etc.). Ultimately, the responsibility of organizing the Australian National Antarctic Research Expeditions (ANARE) is vested in the Director of the Antarctic Division and his staff and the leaders and teams based for a year at a time on Macquarie Island and (formerly) Heard Island, and at Mawson, Davis and Wilkes on the mainland.

Antarctica, as a sphere of influence in weather, is the world's concern. Without international co-operation such as occurred during the recent I.G.Y. period, knowledge of the complex part and pattern of Antarctica's air circulation in that of the world's atmosphere as a whole will not be greatly extended. The I.G.Y. project was the most widespread ever attempted by man on his planet. There was established a living graticule of observers from pole to pole. They inhabited numerous stations as close as possible to selected meridians (as mentioned previously, these were 10°E., 140°E. and 70°-80°W.), so that the air movements between poles and the Equator could be assessed more fully than ever before. It was the only way to test and confirm the brilliant speculation of men like Dr G. C. Simpson, who, in the lonely days of Scott's last expedition, could scarcely have dreamed of such vindication. The time will come when not only will the buffeting of the concentric air waves of Antarctica upon the systems of other latitudes be accurately plotted, but the breaking of those waves will be forecast when, for various reasons, they become unstable and send displacing surges of bitter air thousands of miles northward. Long-range seasonal weather forecasts could, of course, be of incalculable value to farmers everywhere. An accurate knowledge of the annual dispositions of the upper winds and "jet streams"—some of which are both powerful and constant—must be of great assistance to stratospheric aviation.

Men gather their weather information in a number of ways. They measure its elements—temperature, air pressure and humidity—by reading carefully screened instruments at ground-level and by receiving the same kind of information continuously and automatically by radio signals from balloons rising steadily to heights of a hundred thousand or more feet. They record weather itself in the form of wind, rain or snow, frost or sunshine, and the symptoms of weather in cloud formations, by using other instruments and visual observations. Then they dispatch synopses of atmospheric conditions to mother stations or centres, where a clear picture of systems and weather fronts and movements may be synthesized. Out of a sufficiency of such data, especially if gathered simultaneously over a wide area through the years, major trends and cycles gradually appear.

It should be remembered, however, that the collection of information depends on the absolute accuracy and devotion of men in the field. They must stagger in the white gloom of blizzard along rope life-lines to reach their instruments;

they must peer for hours through theodolite telescopes, standing virtually in the open air, to follow the flight of small pilot balloons indicating high wind movements. The hydrogen gas for the big radiosonde balloons in many cases has to be generated in heavy steel cylinders, and the work requires not only muscle and patience but acute watchfulness. To convert ice to the near boiling water required for the reaction is itself a major task. And, then, to release the vulnerable balloons, five to seven feet in diameter, with precious instruments attached to them, in a gale of wind requires consummate technique. Usually, a man must run downwind, gradually paying out the balloon until he can release the transmitter; a false move in this game and hours of work and expensive instruments may be lost. Yet some parties of meteorologists have managed to get balloons away on many hundreds of consecutive days. The character of this work is difficult to convey to those who have not experienced the weather of the antarctic latitudes.

Most expeditions are not meteorologically confined to base. A number of automatic out-stations are frequently established at distances of up to fifty or sixty miles. Here instruments record weather automatically, but they must be visited and serviced regularly and the sheets showing the graphed variations (the "traces") of recorder mechanisms must be collected and renewed. This involves real expeditionary work at times, with dog teams, tractors or weasels, over plateau or sea ice, or by aeroplane. Synoptic meteorological observations are made incidentally on all field journeys of exploration, and some excursions and flights are undertaken for the express purpose of obtaining meteorological information.

If the physical demands of the work are considerable, they merely match the intense concentration and purpose required over long periods of the operators of radiosonde and radio-theodolite recording instruments. These may delight the observer by their almost uncanny precision and the complexity of the work they perform, but they need comprehension to unravel their complexities and considerable ability in mechanics and electronics to service them should faults develop. It is symptomatic of our age that even wholly automatic stations, capable of functioning for months at a time and propagating radio impulses which may be interpreted in terms of synoptic weather data, are being set up in Antarctica. One such was established by some of Law's (ANARE) men from the *Thala Dan* at Lewis Islet in Davis Bay, Antarctica, two thousand miles south of Adelaide, in early 1958. Its signals, every six hours, could be intercepted over a wide area of the southern hemisphere. Other automatic stations are being considered.

I have mentioned meteorology in some detail (relative to the size of this book) because other factors, visible and invisible, affecting the earth's surface, atmosphere and inhabitants are investigated by broadly similar means and certainly with the same devotion to the cause of science.

For a very small fraction of man's existence as *homo sapiens* he has been conscious of many forces beyond those manifesting themselves to his senses. It is very curious indeed that the decline of superstition and belief in gods, goblins and fairies has been contemporaneous with the growth of knowledge and faith in powers as invisible and impalpable. The old gods of sunshine, wind, rain and fertility in the fields have been replaced by modern meteorology and agricultural science. The modern conception of matter is becoming—paradoxically, since mass is equated with energy— one of non-material forces. The list of energies possessing no gross manifestation, and of which we have no perceptual sense, has lengthened beyond the belief of medieval man, intrigued and bewildered by the constancy of the magnetic needle (though, perhaps oddly, taking gravitational forces for granted).

Geomagnetism is a science which must be studied all over the earth, but there are important foci in the Arctic and

*ANARE photo: John Béchervaise*

Dog teams, casting long evening shadows, on the last lap of the journey from Mawson to the Taylor Glacier emperor penguin rookery. Not all sea-ice is so smooth or provides such good traction.

Crossing the lower reaches of the Vahsel Glacier, Heard Island. On blue ice —without snow-cover—crevasses and other pitfalls show up clearly and are thus less dangerous than those that are screened.

*ANARE photo: John Béchervaise*

*ANARE photo: John Béchervaise*
Camp on sea-ice during a journey to the Taylor Glacier.

the Antarctic—the magnetic poles which, curiously enough, are by no means constant. Since the existence of these areas, where a magnetic needle tends to point vertically into the surface of the earth, was conceived and their positions were first calculated, they have moved many hundreds of miles. It will be recalled that the urgent ambition of James Ross, one hundred and twenty years ago, was to reach the South Magnetic Pole and so to balance his success in the Arctic. Actually, by the time the area was attained by David, Mawson and Mackay, in 1909, it had migrated by a circuitous course from Gauss's calculated position in 1839 (76°S., 146°E.) northward and east by four degrees of latitude and nine of longitude—a distance of some hundreds of miles. Continuing its cyclic movement, it has now almost reached the coast near Mawson's Commonwealth Bay—a movement of four hundred miles in fifty years. Annually, in terms of angular change in magnetic declination all over the world, this movement is slight and fairly constant for long periods, but its assessment, even for navigational purposes, is still important. The magnetic behaviour of the earth might be taken to imply the presence of a great bar magnet lying close to the axis of its spin (which itself is not quite constant). The shift of the dip pole is considered a local and superficial phenomenon.

The nature of the world's magnetic forces, which extend far into space in fields of power capable of deflecting streams of particles from the sun or outer space, is not fully comprehended. The vast cage of magnetic energy is almost entirely of terrestrial origin; a very small percentage, associated with the electrified ionosphere, is induced. But, in the manner of the lines of force demonstrable by a simple bar magnet, those of the earth converge to poles and deflect thither electrified cosmic or solar particles. It is the interaction of all these in themes and systems that draws scientists to the polar regions, where important aspects may be best studied.

H

The magnetic forces of the earth are investigated in close association with other phenomena such as auroral displays and ionospheric effects, with both of which they are evidently related. Hundreds, perhaps thousands, of miles from the earth's surface, they provide paths for the charged atomic or sub-atomic particles entering the earth's sphere of influence. Many of these particles are undoubtedly of solar origin and show fluctuations corresponding to sun-spot cycles and flare activity on the sun's surface. As in meteorology, the storms, the anomalies and the unusual surges upsetting the normal course and patterns of these invisible forces provide the best opportunities of learning more concerning their nature. These are more apparent in the polar regions than anywhere else.

Extremely sensitive instruments have been invented to record fluctuations in terrestrial magnetism. Modern variometers consist of minute mirrors, attached to delicately suspended magnets, which reflect accurately aligned beams of light onto slowly revolving cylinders faced with light-sensitized paper. When these traces are developed, they show a continuous record in graphical form of the magnetic variations, and these may be scaled, from time to time, against standard readings taken upon "absolute" instruments by skilled observers. There are well-known daily and seasonal variations; upon these are superimposed the magnetic storms, which themselves, to an extent, occur in cycles that may be related to features on the revolving surface of the sun. Continuous observations all over the world, timed with the utmost precision, prove that these storms are frequently of simultaneous onset.

They often coincide with magnificent displays of the aurora in both hemispheres. These are apparently caused by the streams of electrically charged particles affecting those of the high atmosphere—probably very low concentrations of oxygen atoms—which then part with their energy spontaneously as visible light rather than by imparting it as motion to other atoms. The disposition of these streams is largely governed by the magnetic fields as they exist for hundreds of miles above the surface of the earth. Such an explanation of the aurora, and the analogy commonly drawn between it and the light emitted by tubes of neon gas passing an electric current at low pressure, is currently satisfactory. The geographical distribution of the aurora is also clearly enough governed by the magnetic force in the rare upper atmosphere, surrounding the geomagnetic poles of the earth —which, incidentally, have theoretical positions that do not coincide with those of the actual magnetic poles as indicated on the surface of the globe. The zones from which aurorae are best seen in the zenith form approximately circular bands round these geomagnetic poles, at a distance from them of about twenty-three degrees (about fifteen hundred miles). It happens that the ANARE stations at both Macquarie Island and Mawson are very close to the auroral zone, and provide excellent positions of observation.

At such stations auroral displays are visible on most dark cloudless nights. Much work is being undertaken in photo-graphing the formations and, by simultaneous exposures from two distant points, in calculating their heights. The auroral physicist, preoccupied as he must be by abstruse considerations of spatial and temporal distribution and the nature of this particular manifestation of energy, is nevertheless conscious of the direct appeal to the imagination of the colours, forms and movements of the spectacle. Bows of pulsating greenish light span the horizon, break up into rays, re-gather and form curtains and ribbons with incredible speed, become tinged with crimson, occasionally with violet, move restlessly over the stars, sometimes outshining them by their brilliance. Although the forms of the aurora may be classified, and the causes may be explicable, the sight of the sky streaming with light is always astonishing and, to the majority of men, awesome. As visible symptoms of ionos-pheric conditions, as correlatives of magnetic storm and dislocation of radio services, the aurorae, both borealis and australis, will continue to be investigated quite dispassionately, but as natural phenomena of surpassing beauty and majesty they will always be exciting to everyone who travels in high latitudes.

The various electrified layers of the ionosphere, and the passage through them of cosmic particles of constant or changing nature, are all of immense importance in this atomic age. Several concentric levels, differing in electronic character and ranging up to at least three hundred miles above the surface of the earth, have been detected. One valuable quality possessed by the ionosphere is its disposition to reflect short-wave radio signals back to earth, thus allowing impulses to travel round the world in a series of "bounces" between the earth and the electrically charged "F" layer. This convenient effect is not constant. Sometimes radio signals are not reflected and there is a radio "blackout". The height of the "F" layer does, of course, influence the length of the bounce, and at certain distances signals may be inaudible owing to a "skip" effect. Poor radio propagation is not infrequently accompanied by unusually vivid aurorae and strong magnetic disturbances. It is obvious that all these phenomena must be studied for their own sake as well as for any technological benefits conferred on mankind. Yet there is inspiration in the thought that ionospheric research was the father of modern radar.

Another energy reaching the earth is that of cosmic "rays", particles entering the earth's upper atmosphere at high velocities from outer space and undergoing nuclear transmutations before reaching its surface. The study of cosmic radiation has added immensely to man's knowledge of atomic and especially nuclear physics, indeed to his whole conception and comprehension of the nature of physical substance. The tremendous advances of the last twenty years, the frightening power of atomic weapons, the vision of man's control over resources undreamed of a generation ago, culminating in the production of power from the fission of complex, or the fusion of simpler, elements—all are related quite directly to contributions from the studies of cosmic radiation. The primary cosmic particles affect and are affected by the atoms of the earth's upper atmosphere. Some of the latter are actually transmuted into other elements, carbon, for instance, being produced from nitrogen (both the carbon and the nitrogen are rare isotopes or forms of the elements). It was the investigation of "natural" radioactivity and of radioactive transmutations which led to the Joliots' discovery of "artificial" radioactivity in 1934.

I have done little more than hint at the vast and complex scientific programme of the nations interested in Antarctica. My survey has not been exhaustive even in summary; no mention has been made, for instance, of gravitational, seismic and geodetic calculations. The knowledge sought is not easier to obtain than that concerning the tangible nature and resources of the great white continent. Those expedition members whose task is geology, glaciology or mapping are explorers in visible media. They will not rest content until they know how Antarctica is formed and what minerals exist there both above and below its ice; how the ice-sheet moves and what is its thickness and general heat and mass economy; how it is shaped precisely in every dimension. All these matters are being investigated with the aid of devices of modern invention. The geologist has his geiger counters and scintillometers (which detect radioactive minerals from the air), and he makes use of knowledge of anomalies in gravitational and geomagnetic forces to discover variations in crustal structure. The glaciologist uses seismic sounding for depth determinations and complex laboratory tests to find out the behaviour of ice under changing temperatures and pressures. The cartographer possesses instruments of almost unimaginable precision; he times the passage of light in order to measure distance, and his eyes have the range and vision of the modern aerial cameras that take continuous overlapping photographs from three angles at once. Much of the work in all these sciences is still arduous, uncomfortable and dangerous. It often seems as though the gods and demons of uncreated antarctic myths await the unwary modern explorer behind his facade of insulation, speed and mechanics.

Intentionally I have played down the mineral wealth of Antarctica. There are sufficient indications that it exists. Hundreds of economically valuable minerals have been discovered in small quantities, but, of course, even today, only a limited percentage of the area of Antarctica has been visited. It is possible that the sulphides of the South Shetlands and of the mountains of Marie Byrd Land may be the first discoveries to be followed up economically. In recent years the belief that oil exists below rock or ice has been buttressed by critical examination of the formations. But it must be baldly stated that mineral deposits of any kind, however rich, must be equated with the economics of mining and refining and transport. However, there are complexes of power which were, until recently, beyond the dreams of science. The realization of the full potentialities of Antarctica may await the day when its refrigeration and unlimited water will be valuable factors in its development. We live in an age of atoms and satellites. Antarctica, at this long last, could become a bitter testing ground of the strength of national rivalries and ambitions—or it could provide a vast international laboratory for the study of geophysics, whose language is universal and whose achievements are a common heritage of humanity.

# POSTSCRIPT

Once more I have returned from Antarctica, in time to add a few words to this little book before it is printed. The results of the I.G.Y. have already proved so valuable and stimulating that many nations are continuing their scientific programmes in Antarctica in order to obtain and examine data over longer periods. An international pact has been signed by all the interested powers, promising the development of the far south for peaceful purposes only, its freedom for physicists and explorers of all lands to investigate its phenomena, and the "freezing", for the time being, of all contemporary territorial claims. There can be none who has served in Antarctica who will not echo the hope of Lord Casey, formerly Australian Minister for External Affairs, that the treaty will establish "a permanent Pax Antarctica".

J.M.B.

*Belmont, Victoria,*
1960.

# APPENDIX: SPECIES OF
# ANTARCTIC MAMMALS AND BIRDS

## MAMMALS
### SEALS

| | |
|---|---|
| crabeater seal | *Lobodon carcinophagus* |
| elephant seal | *Mirounga leonina* |
| Hooker's sea-lion | *Phocarctos hookeri* |
| leopard seal (sea-leopard) | *Hydrurga leptonyx* |
| Ross seal | *Ommatophoca rossi* |
| South Australian sea-lion | *Neophoca cinerea* |
| southern fur seal | *Arctocephalus australis** |
| southern sea-lion | *Otaria byroni* |
| Weddell seal | *Leptonychotes weddelli* |

* There are probably two or three closely related species.

### WHALES

| | |
|---|---|
| blue whale | *Balaenoptera musculus* |
| fin whale | *Balaenoptera physalus* |
| humpback whale | *Megaptera nodosa* |
| killer whale | *Orca gladiator* |
| right whale | *Eubalaena australis* |
| sei whale | *Balaenoptera borealis* |
| sperm whale | *Physeter catodon* |

## BIRDS
### PENGUINS

| | |
|---|---|
| Adélie penguin | *Pygoscelis adeliae* |
| emperor penguin | *Aptenodytes forsteri* |
| gentoo penguin | *Pygoscelis papua* |
| king penguin | *Aptenodytes patagonica* |
| macaroni penguin | *Eudyptes chrysolophus chrysolophus* |
| ring or chinstrap penguin | *Pygoscelis antarctica* |
| rockhopper penguin | *Eudyptes chrysocome* |
| royal penguin | *Eudyptes chrysolophus schlegeli* |

## Albatrosses

black-browed albatross  *Diomedea melanophris*
light-mantled sooty albatross  *Phoebetria palpebrata*
wandering albatross  *Diomedea exulans*

## Petrels

antarctic petrel  *Thalassoica antarctica*
cape pigeon  *Daption capensis*
dove prion  *Pachyptila desolata*
giant petrel  *Macronectes giganteus*
silver-grey petrel  *Fulmarus glacialoides*
snow petrel  *Pagodroma nivea*
Wilson's black and white  *Oceanites oceanicus*
  storm petrel

## Gulls, Skuas

Dominican gull  *Larus dominicanus*
McCormick skua  *Catharacta maccormicki*
Southern skua  *Catharacta lonnbergi*

## Terns

antarctic tern  *Sterna vittata vittata*
arctic tern*  *Sterna macrura*

\* Visits antarctic waters for the southern summer.

## Sheathbill

Heard Island sheathbill  *Chionis minor nasicornis*

# AN ANTARCTIC READING LIST

The following list of books on Antarctica, which is chronological, attempts to include a representative library of the standard works in English and of contemporary works describing the situation existing today. It cannot, of course, be regarded as definitive; all the volumes mentioned will, however, be found in most of the larger public libraries.

1876 W. J. J. SPRY, The Cruise of Her Majesty's Ship *Challenger*.
1900 F. A. COOK, Through the First Antarctic Night, 1898-1899 (*Belgica* expedition).
1901 C. E. BORCHGREVINK, First on the Antarctic Continent (expedition of 1898-1900).
1905 H. R. MILL, The Siege of the South Pole.
1905 N. OTTO G. NORDENSKJÖLD and J. G. ANDERSSON, Antarctica; or, Two years amongst the ice of the South Pole.
1905 R. F. SCOTT, The Voyage of the *Discovery* (2 vols).
1906 R. N. RUDMOSE-BROWN *et al.*, The Voyage of the *Scotia* (Bruce, 1902-4).
1909 ERNEST H. SHACKLETON, The Heart of the Antarctic (British expedition, 1907-9; 2 vols).
1911 J. B. CHARCOT (trans. P. Walsh), The Voyage of the *Why Not?* (1908-10).
1912 ROALD E. G. AMUNDSEN, The South Pole (Norwegian expedition, 1910-12; 2 vols).
1913 L. HUXLEY (arr.), Scott's Last Expedition (vol. 1: Journals of Captain R. F. Scott; vol. 2: Reports of the journeys and the scientific work undertaken by Dr E. A. Wilson and the surviving members of the expedition).
1914 R. E. PRIESTLEY, Antarctic Adventure: Scott's northern party.
1915 DOUGLAS MAWSON, The Home of the Blizzard (Australasian expedition, 1911-14; 2 vols).
1919 J. K. DAVIS, With the *Aurora* in the Antarctic, 1911-14.
1920 ERNEST H. SHACKLETON, South (British expedition, 1914-17).
1921 E. R. G. R. EVANS, South with Scott.
1921 H. G. PONTING, The Great White South.
1922 A. CHERRY-GARRARD, The Worst Journey in the World.
1923 J. R. F. (FRANK) WILD, Shackleton's Last Voyage.
1925 J. F. (FRANK) HURLEY, Argonauts of the South . . . in the Antarctic with Sir Douglas Mawson and Sir Ernest Shackleton.

1925  A. J. VILLIERS, Whaling in the Frozen South (Norwegian whaling expedition, 1923-4).

1928  J. GORDON HAYES, Antarctica.

1930  T. GRIFFITH TAYLOR, Antarctic Adventure and Research.

1931  RICHARD E. BYRD, Little America: Aerial exploration in the Antarctic and the flight to the South Pole.

1932  J. GORDON HAYES, The Conquest of the South Pole: Antarctic exploration, 1906-1931.

1933  G. SEAVER, Edward Wilson of the Antarctic.

1935  LARS CHRISTENSEN, Such is the Antarctic.

1938  RICHARD E. BYRD, Alone.

1938  F. D. OMMANNEY, South Latitude.

1941  RUSSELL OWEN, The Antarctic Ocean.

1948  J. F. (FRANK) HURLEY, Shackleton's Argonauts.

1949  T. R. HENRY, The White Continent.

1949  FINN RONNE, Antarctic Conquest (1946-8).

1950  MOUNTEVANS, 1ST BARON (E. R. G. R. Evans), The Desolate Antarctic.

1951  E. W. HUNTER CHRISTIE, The Antarctic Problem: An historical and political study.

1952  NEW ZEALAND ANTARCTIC SOCIETY (ed. F. A. Simpson), The Antarctic Today: A mid-century survey.

1953  W. ARTHUR SCHOLES, The Seventh Continent: Saga of Australian exploration in Antarctica, 1895-1950.

1954  JOHN GIAEVER, The White Desert (Norwegian-British-Swedish expedition, 1949-52).

1955  W. ROSS COCKRILL, Antarctic Hazard.

1955  E. W. K. WALTON, Two Years in the Antarctic (Falkland Islands Dependencies survey).

1957  ROBERT G. DOVERS, Huskies.

1957  GEORGE DUFEK, Operation Deepfreeze.

1957  MARGERY FISHER and JAMES FISHER, Shackleton.

1957  PHILLIP G. LAW and JOHN M. BÉCHERVAISE, ANARE: Australia's Antarctic Outposts.

1958  COLIN BERTRAM, Arctic and Antarctic: A prospect of the polar regions.

1958  VIVIAN E. FUCHS and EDMUND HILLARY, The Crossing of Antarctica.

1959  FRANK DEBENHAM, Antarctica: The story of a continent.

1959  A. LAURENCE P. KIRWAN, The White Road: A survey of polar exploration.

1959  ALFRED LANSING, Endurance: Shackleton's incredible voyage.

1959  PAUL SIPLE, 90° South: The story of the American South Pole conquest.

ADMIRALTY HYDROGRAPHIC DEPARTMENT, The Antarctic Pilot.

# INDEX

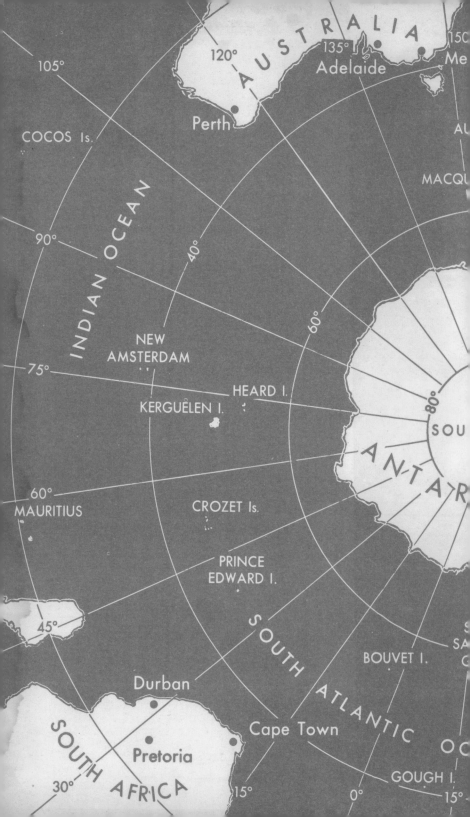